Developmental Mathematics:
A Modular Curriculum for North Carolina
Second Printing

EXPRESSIONS, LINEAR EQUATIONS AND INEQUALITIES

DMA 040

ALAN S. TUSSY
CITRUS COLLEGE

R. DAVID GUSTAFSON
ROCK VALLEY COLLEGE

DIANE R. KOENIG
ROCK VALLEY COLLEGE

BROOKS/COLE
CENGAGE Learning·

Brazil • Japan • Korea • Mexico • Singapore • Spain • United Kingdom • United States

BROOKS/COLE
CENGAGE Learning·

Developmental Mathematics: A Modular Curriculum for North Carolina, Second Printing: Expressions, Linear Equations and Inequalities
Alan S. Tussy, R. David Gustafson, Diane R. Koenig

Publisher: Charlie Van Wagner

Senior Developmental Editor: Danielle Derbenti

Senior Development Editor for Market Strategies: Rita Lombard

Assistant Editor: Stefanie Beeck

Editorial Assistant: Jennifer Cordoba

Media Editor: Heleny Wong

Marketing Manager: Gordon Lee

Marketing Assistant: Angela Kim

Marketing Communications Manager: Katy Malatesta

Content Project Manager: Jennifer Risden

Creative Director: Rob Hugel

Art Director: Vernon Boes

Print Buyer: Linda Hsu

Rights Acquisitions Account Manager, Text: Mardell Glinksi-Schultz

Rights Acquisitions Account Manager, Image: Don Schlotman

Text Designer: Diane Beasley

Photo Researcher: Bill Smith Group

Illustrators: Lori Heckelman; Graphic World Inc; Integra Software Services

Cover Designers: Ryan and Susan Stranz

Cover Image: Background: © Hemera/Thinkstock. © iStockphoto/Thinkstock.

Compositor: Integra Software Services

For product information and technology assistance, contact us at
Cengage Learning Customer & Sales Support, 1-800-354-9706
For permission to use material from this text or product,
submit all requests online at **www.cengage.com/permissions**
Further permissions questions can be e-mailed to
permissionrequest@cengage.com

ISBN-13: 978-1-285-13424-6

ISBN-10: 1-285-13424-9

Brooks/Cole
20 Davis Drive
Belmont, CA 94002-3098
USA

Cengage Learning is a leading provider of customized learning solutions with office locations around the globe, including Singapore, the United Kingdom, Australia, Mexico, Brazil, and Japan. Locate your local office at **www.cengage.com/global**

Cengage Learning products are represented in Canada by Nelson Education, Ltd.

To learn more about Brooks/Cole, visit **www.cengage.com/brookscole**

Purchase any of our products at your local college store or at our preferred online store **www.CengageBrain.com**

Printed at CLDPC, USA, 06-18

PREFACE

Developmental Mathematics: A Modular Curriculum for North Carolina is a fully integrated learning system that has been aligned to the redesigned curriculum established by the North Carolina Developmental Math Redesign Task Force. With the helpful input from instructors across the state, we have put together a program that presents problems in a meaningful context and explains the "why" behind problem solving in order to promote conceptual and sound mathematical learning. This is one of eight modules for the DMA curriculum, and is supported by a highly customizable online homework system that includes assessment tools, personalized study plans, and algorithmically generated problems to reinforce learning.

One central goal of the North Carolina Redesign Task Force was to create a curriculum with streamlined content in a modular format that could be completed in one academic year. Students can purchase only the modules needed for their developmental math requirements, and can work at a pace that is appropriate for their needs. Instructors can easily use this content with different classroom delivery methods, including self-paced Emporium labs, seated courses, and online or hybrid settings.

Another principle of the new curriculum is to develop students' conceptual understanding of mathematics through the use of contextually based problems. To that end, we have added the following features:

- New **Applied Introductions** have been written to introduce sections that are more applications-driven.
- Within the *Study Sets*, **Applications** problems and examples have been added and written to align with the NCCCS learning outcomes.
- **Concept Extensions** have been written and added to the *Study Sets* to ensure that key concepts meet the NCCCS curriculum.

In addition to new conceptual features that we have written specifically for North Carolina, we have added the following features to help guide students toward mastery of each module:

- **Course Information Sheets** start each module. These offer an explanation of the NCCCS process and ask questions that guide students to the practical knowledge that they will need in order to complete the program.
- **Are You Ready?** quizzes have been added to the beginning of each section to test students on the basic skills they will need in order to be successful with that section.
- **Module Tests**, appearing at the end of each module, have been carefully constructed to include the NCCCS learning outcomes required to pass the mastery test.

All content in these modules is supported by a corresponding prebuilt course in Enhanced WebAssign®, Cengage Learning's powerful online homework solution. Enhanced WebAssign® (EWA) engages students with immediate feedback on algorithmically generated versions of problems for unlimited practice. The *Show My Work* feature allows students to upload a file with the problem worked out, or to use a simple math palette to show their steps–helping you assess whether they understand the steps to solving a problem. The North Carolina EWA course has been prebuilt with a Personalized Study Plan, assignments, homework, and a Pre and Post Test for every module. Instructors can use the prebuilt course as is, or can customize or add material with ease.

A corresponding and fully interactive eBook, the Cengage YouBook, is integrated into the Enhanced WebAssign® course, and offers students convenient access to all module content. This powerful eBook lets you tailor the content to fit your course and provide your students with the ultimate learning experience with note-taking, highlighting, book-marking and search capabilities. Link students to your lecture notes, audio summaries, and engage them through conceptual tutorial videos as well as YouTube clips.

Cengage Learning is committed to providing unparallel service and training for faculty.

- **TeamUP Faculty Programs** help you reach and engage students by offering peer-to-peer consulting on curriculum and assessment, workshops, and professional development conferences.

TeamUP Faculty Program Consultants are a team of educators who understand your challenges whether your classroom is on-ground, online, or both.

Cengage Learning's team of **Faculty Advisors** are full-time educators and expert teachers in a diverse range of subject areas. They are available to share their experience on using Cengage Learning solutions and instructional best practices developed in their own classroom.

Explore all the ways TeamUP Faculty Programs can help you launch a new program or support your continuous improvement efforts. http://www.cengage.com/teamup/programs/ offers service and support from a dedicated team of experts to ensure your success using Enhanced WebAssign, including help with course set up, and more. http://www.cengage.com/coursecare/

TRUSTED FEATURES

- **Study Sets** found in each section offer a multifaceted approach to practicing and reinforcing the concepts taught in each section. They are designed for students to methodically build their knowledge of the section concepts, from basic recall to increasingly complex problem solving, through reading, writing, and thinking mathematically.

  Vocabulary—Each *Study Set* begins with the important *Vocabulary* discussed in that section. The fill-in-the-blank vocabulary problems emphasize the main concepts taught in the chapter and provide the foundation for learning and communicating the language of algebra.

  Concepts—In *Concepts,* students are asked about the specific subskills and procedures necessary to successfully complete the *Guided Practice* and *Try It Yourself* problems that follow.

  Notation—In *Notation,* the students review the new symbols introduced in a section. Often, they are asked to fill in steps of a sample solution. This strengthens their ability to read and write mathematics and prepares them for the *Guided Practice* problems by modeling solution formats.

  Guided Practice—The problems in *Guided Practice* are linked to an associated worked example or objective from that section. This feature promotes student success by referring them to the proper examples if they encounter difficulties solving homework problems.

  Try It Yourself—To promote problem recognition, the *Try It Yourself* problems are thoroughly mixed and are *not* linked to worked examples, giving students an opportunity to practice decision-making and strategy selection as they would when taking a test or quiz.

Applications—The *Applications* provide students the opportunity to apply their newly acquired algebraic skills to relevant and interesting real-life situations.

Writing—The *Writing* problems help students build mathematical communication skills.

Review—The *Review* problems consist of randomly selected problems from previous chapters. These problems are designed to keep students' successfully mastered skills up-to-date before they move on to the next section.

- **Detailed Author Notes** that guide students along in a step-by-step process appear in the solutions to every worked example.
- **Think It Through** features make the connection between mathematics and student life. These relevant topics often require algebra skills from the chapter to be applied to a real-life situation. Topics include tuition costs, student enrollment, job opportunities, credit cards, and many more.
- **Using Your Calculator** is an optional feature that is designed for instructors who wish to use calculators as part of the instruction in this course. This feature introduces keystrokes and shows how scientific and graphing calculators can be used to solve problems. In the *Study Sets,* icons are used to denote problems that may be solved using a calculator.

ACKNOWLEDGMENTS

We want to express our gratitude to all those who helped with this project: Steve Odrich, Mary Lou Wogan, Paul McCombs, Maria H. Andersen, Sheila Pisa, Laurie McManus, Alexander Lee, Ed Kavanaugh, Karl Hunsicker, Cathy Gong, Dave Ryba, Terry Damron, Marion Hammond, Lin Humphrey, Doug Keebaugh, Robin Carter, Tanja Rinkel, Bob Billups, Jeff Cleveland, Jo Morrison, Sheila White, Jim McClain, Paul Swatzel, Matt Stevenson, Carole Carney, Joyce Low, Rob Everest, David Casey, Heddy Paek, Ralph Tippins, Mo Trad, Eagle Zhuang, and the Citrus College library staff (including Barbara Rugeley) for their help with this project. Your encouragement, suggestions, and insight have been invaluable to us.

We would also like to express our thanks to the Cengage Learning editorial, marketing, production, and design staff for helping us craft this new edition: Danielle Derbenti, Michael Stranz, Kim Fry, Heleny Wong, Charlie Van Wagner, Jill Staut, Liz Kendall, Marc Bove, Gordon Lee, Rita Lombard, Angela Hodge, Angela Kim, Maureen Ross, Jennifer Risden, Vernon Boes, Diane Beasley, Carol O'Connell, Graphic World and Integra Software Services.

Additionally, we would like to say that authoring a textbook is a tremendous undertaking. Producing a product of this scale that is customized to match a brand new curriculum would not have been possible without the thoughtful feedback and support from the following colleagues from throughout North Carolina listed below. Their contributions to this edition have shaped the creation of this book in countless ways.

A special acknowledgment is due to Lisa Key Brown, of Central Carolina Community College. Lisa's experience in the Developmental Math classroom, detailed knowledge of the new North Carolina curriculum, and expertise in using Enhanced WebAssign has been invaluable to us as we have prepared this developmental math program.

Alan S. Tussy
R. David Gustafson
Diane R. Koenig

Patricia C. Rome, *Delgado Community College*
Patricia B. Roux, *Delgado Community College*
Rebecca Rozario, *Brookdale Community College*
John Squires, *Cleveland State Community College*
Sharon Testone, *Onondaga Community College*
Bill Thompson, *Red Rocks Community College*
Barbara Tozzi, *Brookdale Community College*
Donna Tupper, *Community College of Baltimore County–Essex*
Andreana Walker, *Calhoun Community College*
Jane Wampler, *Housatonic Community College*
Arminda Wey, *Brookdale Community College*
Mary Lou Wogan, *Klamath Community College*
Valerie Wright, *Central Piedmont Community College*
Kevin Yokoyama, *College of the Redwoods*
Mary Young, *Brookdale Community College*

ABOUT THE AUTHORS

Alan S. Tussy

Alan Tussy teaches all levels of developmental mathematics at Citrus College in Glendora, California. He has written nine math books—a paperback series and a hardcover series. A meticulous, creative, and visionary teacher who maintains a keen focus on his students' greatest challenges, Alan Tussy is an extraordinary author, dedicated to his students' success. Alan received his Bachelor of Science degree in Mathematics from the University of Redlands and his Master of Science degree in Applied Mathematics from California State University, Los Angeles. He has taught up and down the curriculum from Prealgebra to Differential Equations. He is currently focusing on the developmental math courses. Professor Tussy is a member of the American Mathematical Association of Two-Year Colleges.

R. David Gustafson

R. David Gustafson is Professor Emeritus of Mathematics at Rock Valley College in Illinois and coauthor of several best-selling math texts, including Gustafson/Frisk's *Beginning Algebra, Intermediate Algebra, Beginning and Intermediate Algebra: A Combined Approach, College Algebra,* and the Tussy/Gustafson developmental mathematics series. His numerous professional honors include Rock Valley Teacher of the Year and Rockford's Outstanding Educator of the Year. He earned a Master of Arts from Rockford College in Illinois, as well as a Master of Science from Northern Illinois University.

Diane R. Koenig

Diane Koenig received a Bachelor of Science degree in Secondary Math Education from Illinois State University in 1980. She began her career at Rock Valley College in 1981, when she became the Math Supervisor for the newly formed Personalized Learning Center. Earning her Master's Degree in Applied Mathematics from Northern Illinois University, Ms. Koenig in 1984 had the distinction of becoming the first full-time woman mathematics faculty member at Rock Valley College. In addition to being nominated for AMATYC's Excellence in Teaching Award, Diane Koenig was chosen as the Rock Valley College Faculty of the Year by her peers in 2005, and, in 2006, she was awarded the NISOD Teaching Excellence Award as well as the Illinois Mathematics Association of Community Colleges Award for Teaching Excellence. In addition to her teaching, Ms. Koenig has been an active member of the Illinois Mathematics Association of Community Colleges (IMACC). As a member, she has served on the board of directors, on a state-level task force rewriting the course outlines for the developmental mathematics courses, and as the association's newsletter editor.

Module 4: Expressions, Linear Equations, and Linear Inequalities

© iStockphoto.com/Kirby Hamilton

from *Campus to Careers*

Registered Dietitian

One of the most important things that you can do to protect yourself from cancer, diabetes, heart disease, and stroke is to eat right. No one knows this better than dietitians. They work in hospitals, health care centers, schools, and correctional facilities, where they plan dietary programs and supervise the preparation of healthy meals. The job of dietitian requires mathematical skills such as calculating calorie intake, analyzing the nutritional content of food, and budgeting for the purchase of groceries and supplies.

Problem 83 in **Study Set 4.5** and **problem 49** in **Study Set 4.7** involve situations that a registered dietitian might encounter on the job. The mathematical concepts discussed in this module can be used to solve those problems.

JOB TITLE: Registered Dietitian

EDUCATION: A bachelor's degree in foods and nutrition (or a related field) and supervised practice

JOB OUTLOOK: Growth faster than the average, 18%–26% increase

ANNUAL EARNINGS: The median base salary in 2010 was $53,250.

FOR MORE INFORMATION: www.bls.gov/oco/ocos077.htm

Course Information Sheet

Overview

Module 4: Expressions, Linear Equations, and Linear Inequalities is one of the eight modules that make up the North Carolina Community College System Developmental Math Program. This program is for students who want to meet the prerequisites for the math requirements for their two year degree, or for those who are planning to transfer to a college or university. It is designed to allow you to complete the required developmental math courses at a pace that is appropriate to your needs and knowledge.

Placement

The diagnostic test that you took to enter the NCCCS Developmental Math Program has indentified your mathematical strengths and weaknesses. The test results that you received indicate which of the eight modules you are required to complete before you can enroll in more advanced mathematics courses, such as Precalculus and Statistics. It is important to note that any modules you are required to take must be taken in numerical order. For example, if the diagnostic test indicated that you need to take Modules 4 and 5, you must successfully complete Module 4 before you can register for Module 5.

Mastery

A core principle of the NCCCS Developmental Math Program is the concept of mastery of the material. To show mastery, students need to successfully complete all coursework in a module, as well as pass a final assessment exam.

Getting started

Starting a new course can be exciting, but it might also make you a bit nervous. In order to be successful, you need a plan. Here are some suggestions: Make time for the course, know what is expected, build a support system. You can begin to form your personal plan for success by answering questions on the next page.

©iStockphoto/Thinkstock

1. What is your instructor's name? What is his/her phone number and email address?

2. When and where does your class meet?

3. What are the days and times of your instructor's office hours? Where does he/she hold office hours?

4. Does your campus have a math tutoring center? If so, where is it located and what are its hours of operation? Is the tutoring free? Do you need your instructor to sign a form before you begin at the tutoring center?

5. What other ways are there for you to receive additional help with this module?

6. What are the names, phone numbers, and email addresses of three students in your class that you can contact for help if you have missed class, want to form a study group, or have questions regarding a homework assignment?

7. How many hours does your instructor feel you should expect to spend on this course each week?

8. Did you write down your WebAssign user id and password in a safe place where you can find it should you forget?

9. On what day and at what time is the final module assessment exam?

10. What percent correct is needed to pass the final module assessment exam? How many times can the final assessment exam be taken?

Objectives

1. Identify terms and coefficients of terms.
2. Write word phrases as algebraic expressions.
3. Analyze problems to determine hidden operations.
4. Evaluate algebraic expressions.

SECTION 4.1

Algebraic Expressions

ARE YOU READY?

▼ *The following problems review some basic concepts that are important when working with algebraic expressions.*

Write each expression in simpler form.

1. $9 \cdot x$ **2.** $1 \cdot m$ **3.** $-1 \cdot t$ **4.** $\dfrac{7}{8} \cdot y$

Identify each of the following expressions as either a sum, difference, product, or quotient.

5. $\dfrac{x}{12}$ **6.** $45 - a$ **7.** $2bc$ **8.** $d + 5$

Since problems in algebra are often presented in words, the ability to understand what you read is important. In this section, we will introduce several strategies that will help you translate English words into mathematical symbols.

1 Identify terms and coefficients of terms.

In algebra, we use symbols such as x and y to represent unknown numbers. A symbol that is used to represent a number is called a **variable**.

> ### Algebraic Expressions
>
> Variables and/or numbers can be combined with the operations of addition, subtraction, multiplication, and division to create **algebraic expressions**.

Here are some other examples of algebraic expressions.

$4a + 7$ — This expression is a combination of the numbers 4 and 7, the variable a, and the operations of multiplication and addition.

$\dfrac{10 - y}{3}$ — This expression is a combination of the numbers 10 and 3, the variable y, and the operations of subtraction and division.

$15mn(2m)$ — This expression is a combination of the numbers 15 and 2, the variables m and n, and the operation of multiplication.

Addition symbols separate algebraic expressions into parts called *terms*. For example, the expression $x + 8$ has two terms.

$$\underset{\text{First term}}{x} \quad + \quad \underset{\text{Second term}}{8}$$

Since subtraction can be written as addition of the opposite, the expression $a^2 - 3a - 9$ has three terms.

$$a^2 - 3a - 9 = \underset{\text{First term}}{a^2} \quad + \quad \underset{\text{Second term}}{(-3a)} \quad + \quad \underset{\text{Third term}}{(-9)}$$

In general, a **term** is a product or quotient of numbers and/or variables. A single number or variable is also a term. Examples of terms are:

$$4, \quad y, \quad 6r, \quad -w^3, \quad 3.7x^5, \quad \dfrac{3}{n}, \quad -15ab^2$$

The Language of Algebra   By the commutative property of multiplication, $r6 = 6r$ and $-15b^2a = -15ab^2$. However, we usually write the numerical factor first and the variable factors in alphabetical order.

The numerical factor of a term is called the **coefficient** of the term. For instance, the term $6r$ has a coefficient of 6 because $6r = 6 \cdot r$. The coefficient of $-15ab^2$ is -15 because $-15ab^2 = -15 \cdot ab^2$. More examples are shown.

A term such as 4, that consists of a single number, is called a **constant term.**

Term	Coefficient	
$8y^2$	8	
$-0.9pq$	-0.9	
$\frac{3}{4}b$	$\frac{3}{4}$	This term could be written $\frac{3b}{4}$.
$-\frac{x}{6}$	$-\frac{1}{6}$	Because $-\frac{x}{6} = -\frac{1x}{6} = -\frac{1}{6} \cdot x$
x	1	Because $x = 1x$
$-t$	-1	Because $-t = -1t$
27	27	

The Language of Algebra   Terms such as x and y have *implied* coefficients of 1. *Implied* means suggested without being precisely expressed.

EXAMPLE 1   Identify the coefficient of each term in the following expression: $7x^2 - x + 6$

Strategy We will begin by writing the subtraction as addition of the opposite. Then we will determine the numerical factor of each term.

WHY Addition symbols separate expressions into terms.

Solution
If we write $7x^2 - x + 6$ as $7x^2 + (-x) + 6$, we see that it has three terms: $7x^2$, $-x$, and 6. The numerical factor of each term is its coefficient.

The coefficient of $7x^2$ is **7** because $7x^2$ means $7 \cdot x^2$.

The coefficient of $-x$ is -1 because $-x$ means $-1 \cdot x$.

The coefficient of the constant 6 is 6.

It is important to be able to distinguish between the *terms* of an expression and the *factors* of a term.

EXAMPLE 2   Is m used as a *factor* or a *term* in each expression?

a. $m + 6$ **b.** $8m$

Strategy We will begin by determining whether m is involved in an addition or a multiplication.

WHY Addition symbols separate expressions into *terms*. A *factor* is a number being multiplied.

Self Check 1
Identify the coefficient of each term in the expression:
$p^3 - 12p^2 + 3p - 4$

Now Try Problem 15

Self Check 2
Is b used as a *factor* or a *term* in each expression?
a. $-27b$
b. $5a + b$

Now Try Problem 21

Solution

a. Since m is added to 6, m is a term of $m + 6$.

b. Since m is multiplied by 8, m is a factor of $8m$.

2 Write word phrases as algebraic expressions.

In the following tables, we list some words and phrases that are used to indicate addition, subtraction, multiplication, and division, and we show how they can be translated to form algebraic expressions.

Addition

The phrase	Translates to
the sum of a and 8	$a + 8$
4 plus c	$4 + c$
16 added to m	$m + 16$
4 more than t	$t + 4$
20 greater than F	$F + 20$
T increased by r	$T + r$
exceeds y by 35	$y + 35$

Subtraction

The phrase	Translates to
the difference of 23 and P	$23 - P$
550 minus h	$550 - h$
18 less than w	$w - 18$
7 decreased by j	$7 - j$
M reduced by x	$M - x$
12 subtracted from L	$L - 12$
5 less f	$5 - f$

> **Caution!** Be careful when translating subtraction. Order is important. For example, when translating the phrase "18 less than w," the terms are reversed.
>
> 18 less than w
>
> $w - 18$

Multiplication

The phrase	Translates to
the product of 4 and x	$4x$
20 times B	$20B$
twice r	$2r$
triple the profit P	$3P$
$\frac{3}{4}$ of m	$\frac{3}{4}m$

Division

The phrase	Translates to
the quotient of R and 19	$\dfrac{R}{19}$
s divided by d	$\dfrac{s}{d}$
the ratio of c to d	$\dfrac{c}{d}$
k split into 4 equal parts	$\dfrac{k}{4}$

> **Caution!** The phrase *greater than* is used to indicate addition. The phrase *is greater than* refers to the symbol $>$. Similarly, the phrase *less than* indicates subtraction, and the phrase *is less than* refers to the symbol $<$.

EXAMPLE 3   Write each phrase as an algebraic expression.

a. The sum of the length l and the width 20

b. 5 less than the capacity c

c. The product of the weight w and 2,000, increased by 300

Strategy We will read each phrase and pay close attention to key words that can be translated to mathematical operations. We will refer to the tables as a guide if needed.

WHY Key phrases can be translated to mathematical symbols.

Solution

a. Key word: *sum*   **Translation:** add

The phrase translates to $l + 20$.

b. Key phrase: *less than*   **Translation:** subtract

The capacity c is to be made less, so we subtract 5 from it: $c - 5$.

c. Key word: *product*   **Translation:** multiply

Key phrase: *increased by*   **Translation:** add

The weight w is to be multiplied by 2,000, and then 300 is to be added to the product: $2,000w + 300$.

When solving problems, we often begin by letting a variable stand for an unknown quantity.

EXAMPLE 4   *Food Preparation*   A butcher trims 4 ounces of fat from a roast that originally weighed x ounces. Write an algebraic expression that represents the weight of the roast after it is trimmed.

Strategy We will start by letting x represent the original weight of the roast. Then we will look for a key word or phrase to write an expression that represents the trimmed weight of the roast.

WHY The weight after trimming is related to the original weight of the roast.

Solution

We let $x =$ the original weight of the roast (in ounces).

Key word: *trimmed*   **Translation:** subtract

After 4 ounces of fat have been trimmed, the weight of the roast is $(x - 4)$ ounces. ∎

EXAMPLE 5   *Competitive Swimming*   The swimming pool to the right is x feet wide. If it is to be sectioned into 8 equally wide swimming lanes, write an algebraic expression that represents the width of each lane.

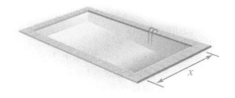

Strategy We start by letting x represent the width of the swimming pool. Then we will look for key words or phrases to write an expression that represents the width of each lane.

WHY The width of each lane is related to the width of the pool.

Solution

We let $x =$ the width of the swimming pool (in feet).

Key phrase: *sectioned into 8 equally wide lanes*   **Translation:** divide

The width of each lane is $\dfrac{x}{8}$ feet.

When we are solving problems, the variable to be used is rarely specified. We must decide what the unknown quantities are and how they will be represented using variables. The following examples illustrate how to approach these situations.

Self Check 6

A candy bar has twice the number of calories as a serving of pears. Write an expression that represents the number of calories in a candy bar.

Now Try **Problem 47**

EXAMPLE 6   *Collectibles*   The value of a collectible doll is three times that of an antique toy truck. Write an expression that represents the value of the doll.

Strategy We start by letting x represent the value of the toy truck. Then we will look for key words or phrases to write an expression that represents the value of the antique doll.

WHY The value of the doll is related to the value of the toy truck.

Solution
There are two unknown quantities. Since the doll's value is related to the truck's value, we will let x = the value of the toy truck in dollars.

Key phrase: 3 *times*   **Translation:** multiply by 3

The value of the doll is $\$3x$.

> *Caution!*   A variable is used to represent an unknown number. Therefore, in Example 6, it would be incorrect to write, "Let x = toy truck," because the truck is not a number. We need to write, "Let x = the *value* of the toy truck."

Self Check 7

Part of a $900 donation to a college went to the scholarship fund, the rest to the building fund. Choose a variable to represent the amount donated to one of the funds. Then write an expression that represents the amount donated to the other fund.

Now Try **Problem 52**

EXAMPLE 7   *Painting*   A 10-inch-long paintbrush has two parts: a handle and bristles. Choose a variable to represent the length of one of the parts. Then write an expression to represent the length of the other part.

Strategy There are two approaches. We can let h = the length of the handle or we can let b = the length of the bristles.

WHY Both the length of the handle and the length of the bristles are unknown, however we do know the entire length of the paintbrush.

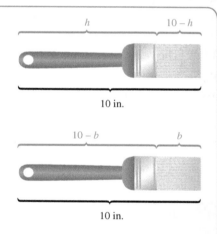

Solution
Refer to the drawing on the top. If we let h = the length of the handle (in inches), then the length of the bristles is $10 - h$.

Now refer to the drawing on the bottom. If we let b = the length of the bristles (in inches), then the length of the handle is $10 - b$.

Self Check 8

The number of votes received by the incumbent in an election was 55 fewer than three times the number the challenger received. Write an expression that represents the number of votes received by the incumbent.

Now Try **Problem 53**

EXAMPLE 8   *Student Enrollments*   In the second semester, student enrollment in a retraining program at a college was 32 more than twice that of the first semester. Write an expression that represents the student enrollment in the second semester.

Strategy We start by letting x represent the enrollment in the first semester. Then we will look for a key word or phrase to write an expression to represent the second-semester enrollment.

WHY The second-semester enrollment is related to the first-semester enrollment.

Solution

Since the second-semester enrollment is expressed in terms of the first-semester enrollment, we let x = the enrollment in the first semester.

Key phrase: *more than*   **Translation:** add

Key word: *twice*   **Translation:** multiply by 2

The enrollment for the second semester is $2x + 32$.

3 Analyze problems to determine hidden operations.

When analyzing problems, we aren't always given key words or key phrases to help establish what mathematical operation to use. Sometimes a careful reading of the problem is needed to determine the hidden operations.

EXAMPLE 9   *Disney Theme Parks*   Disneyland, located in Anaheim, California, was in operation 16 years before the opening of Walt Disney World, in Orlando, Florida. Euro Disney, in Paris, France, was constructed 21 years after Disney World. Use algebraic expressions to express the ages (in years) of each of these Disney attractions.

Strategy We start by letting x represent the age of Disney World.

WHY The ages of Disneyland and Euro Disney are related to the age of Disney World.

Solution

The ages of Disneyland and Euro Disney are both related to the age of Walt Disney World. Therefore, we will let x = the age of Walt Disney World.

In carefully reading the problem, we find that Disneyland was built 16 years *before* Disney World, so its age is more than that of Disney World.

Key phrase: *more than*   **Translation:** add

In years, the age of Disneyland is $x + 16$. Euro Disney was built 21 years *after* Disney World, so its age is less than that of Disney World.

Key phrase: *less than*   **Translation:** subtract

In years, the age of Euro Disney is $x - 21$. The results are summarized in the table.

Attraction	Age
Disneyland	$x + 16$
Disney World	x
Euro Disney	$x - 21$

EXAMPLE 10   How many months are in x years?

Strategy There are no key words, so we must carefully analyze the problem to write an expression that represents the number of months in x years. We will begin by considering some specific cases.

WHY When no key words are present, it is helpful to work with specifics to get a better understanding of the relationship between the two quantities.

Solution

Let's calculate the number of months in 1 year, 2 years, and 3 years. When we write the results in a table, a pattern is apparent.

Self Check 9

TAX PREPARATION Kayla worked 5 more hours preparing her tax return than she did on her daughter's return. Kayla's son's return took her 2 more hours to prepare than her daughter's. Write an expression to represent the hours she spent on each return.

Now Try Problem 57

Self Check 10

Complete the table. How many days is h hours?

Number of hours	Number of days
24	
48	
72	
h	

Now Try **Problem 59**

Number of years	Number of months
1	12
2	24
3	36
x	$12x$

We multiply the number of years
by 12 to find the number of months.

Therefore, if x = the number of years, the number of months is $12 \cdot x$ or $12x$.

Some problems deal with quantities that have value. In these problems, we must distinguish between *the number of* and *the value of* the unknown quantity. For example, to find the value of 3 quarters, we multiply the number of quarters by the value (in cents) of one quarter. Therefore, the value of 3 quarters is $3 \cdot 25$ cents = 75 cents.

The same distinction must be made if the number is unknown. For example, the value of n nickels is not n cents. The value of n nickels is $n \cdot 5$ cents = $(5n)$ cents. For problems of this type, we will use the relationship

Number · value = total value

Self Check 11

Find the value of
a. six fifty-dollar savings bonds
b. t one-hundred-dollar savings bonds
c. $x - 4$ one-thousand-dollar savings bonds

Now Try **Problem 62**

EXAMPLE 11   Find the total value of
a. five dimes   **b.** q quarters   **c.** $x + 1$ half-dollars

Strategy We will find the total value (in cents) of each collection of coins by multiplying the number of coins by the value of one coin.

WHY Number · value = total value

Solution
To find the total value (in cents) of each collection of coins, we multiply the number of coins by the value (in cents) of one coin, as shown in the table.

Type of Coin	Number	· Value	= Total Value	
Dime	5	10	50	
Quarter	q	25	$25q$	← $q \cdot 25$ is written $25q$.
Half-dollar	$x + 1$	50	$50(x + 1)$	

---

4 **Evaluate algebraic expressions.**

To **evaluate an algebraic expression,** we replace each variable with a given number value. (When we replace a variable with a number, we say we are **substituting** for the variable.) Then we do the necessary calculations following the rules for the order of operations. For example, to evaluate $x^2 - 2x + 1$ for $x = 3$, we begin by substituting 3 for x.

$$x^2 - 2x + 1 = 3^2 - 2(3) + 1 \qquad \text{Substitute 3 for } x.$$
$$= 9 - 2(3) + 1 \qquad \text{Evaluate the exponential expression: } 3^2 = 9.$$
$$= 9 - 6 + 1 \qquad \text{Perform the multiplication: } 2(3) = 6.$$
$$= 4 \qquad \text{Working left to right, perform the subtraction and then the addition.}$$

We say that 4 is the **value** of this expression when $x = 3$.

Caution!   When replacing a variable with its numerical value, use parentheses around the replacement number to avoid possible misinterpretation. For example, when substituting 5 for x in $2x + 1$, we show the multiplication using parentheses: $2(5) + 1$. If we don't show the multiplication, we could misread the expression as $25 + 1$.

EXAMPLE 12   Evaluate each expression for $x = 3$ and $y = -4$:
a. $-y$ **b.** $-3(y + x^2)$

Strategy We will replace x with 3 and y with -4 and then evaluate the expression using the order of operations.

WHY To evaluate an expression means to find its numerical value, once we know the values of the variable(s).

Solution
a. $-y = -(-4)$ Substitute −4 for y.
    $= 4$ The opposite of −4 is 4.
b. $-3(y + x^2) = -3(-4 + 3^2)$ Substitute 3 for x and −4 for y.
    $= -3(-4 + 9)$ Work within the parentheses first. Evaluate the expo-
                      nential expression.
    $= -3(5)$ Perform the addition within the parentheses.
    $= -15$

Self Check 12
Evaluate each expression for $x = -2$ and $y = 3$:   **a.** $-x$ **b.** $5(x - y)$

Now Try **Problem 63**

EXAMPLE 13   *Temperature Conversion* The expression $\frac{9C + 160}{5}$ converts a temperature in degrees Celsius (represented by C) to a temperature in degrees Fahrenheit. Convert $-170°C$, the coldest temperature on the moon, to degrees Fahrenheit.

Strategy We will replace C in the expression with -170 and evaluate it using the order of operations.

WHY The expression evaluated at $C = -170$ converts $-170°C$ to degrees Fahrenheit.

Solution
To convert $-170°C$ to degrees Fahrenheit, we evaluate the algebraic expression for $C = -170$.

$$\frac{9C + 160}{5} = \frac{9(-170) + 160}{5}$$ Substitute −170 for C.

$$= \frac{-1,530 + 160}{5}$$ Perform the multiplication.

$$= \frac{-1,370}{5}$$ Perform the addition.

$$= -274$$ Perform the division.

In degrees Fahrenheit, the coldest temperature on the moon is $-274°$.

Self Check 13
On January 22, 1943, the temperature in Spearfish, South Dakota changed from $-20°C$ to $7.2°C$ in two minutes. Convert $-20°C$ to degrees Fahrenheit.

Now Try **Problem 75**

Using Your CALCULATOR   Evaluating Algebraic Expressions

The rotating drum of a clothes dryer is a cylinder. To find the capacity of the dryer, we can find its volume by evaluating the algebraic expression $\pi r^2 h$, where r represents the radius and h represents the height of the drum. (Here, the cylinder is lying on its side.) If we substitute 13.5 for r and 20 for h, we obtain $\pi(13.5)^2(20)$. Using a scientific calculator, we can evaluate the expression by entering these numbers and pressing these keys.

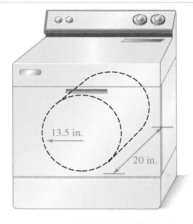

13.5 in.

20 in.

$\boxed{\pi}$ $\boxed{\times}$ 13.5 $\boxed{x^2}$ $\boxed{\times}$ 20 $\boxed{=}$ $\boxed{\text{11451.10522}}$

Using a graphing or direct-entry calculator, we can evaluate the expression by entering these numbers and pressing these keys.

$\boxed{\text{2nd}}$ $\boxed{\pi}$ $\boxed{\times}$ 13.5 $\boxed{x^2}$ $\boxed{\times}$ 20 $\boxed{\text{ENTER}}$

$\boxed{\begin{array}{l}\pi*13.5^2*20\\ \qquad\qquad\qquad \text{11451.10522}\end{array}}$

To the nearest cubic inch, the capacity of the dryer is 11,451 in.^{3}.

Self Check 14

In Example 14, suppose the initial velocity is 112 feet per second, so the height of the rocket is given by $112t - 16t^2$. Complete the table to find out how many seconds after launch it would hit the ground.

t	$112t - 16t^2$
1	
3	
5	
7	

Now Try **Problem 82**

EXAMPLE 14   *Rocketry*   If a toy rocket is shot into the air with an initial velocity of 80 feet per second, its height (in feet) after t seconds in flight is given by the algebraic expression

$$80t - 16t^2$$

How many seconds after the launch will it hit the ground?

Strategy We will substitute positive values for t, the time in flight, until we find the one that gives a height of 0.

WHY When the toy rocket is on the ground, its height above the ground is 0.

Solution
We can substitute positive values for t, the time in flight, until we find the one that gives a height of 0. At that time, the rocket will be on the ground. We will begin by finding the height after the rocket has been in flight for 1 second ($t = 1$) and record the result in a table.

$$80t - 16t^2 = 80(1) - 16(1)^2 \quad \text{\scriptsize Substitute 1 for } t.$$
$$= 64$$

After 1 second in flight, the height of the rocket is 64 feet. We continue to pick more values of t until we find out when the height is 0.

As we evaluate $80t - 16t^2$ for various values of t, we can show the results in a **table of values.** In the column headed "t," we list each value of the variable to be used in the evaluations. In the column headed "$80t - 16t^2$," we write the result of each evaluation.

t	$80t - 16t^2$
1	64
2	96
3	96
4	64
5	0

Evaluate for $t = 2$:
$80t - 16t^2 = 80(2) - 16(2)^2 = 96$
Evaluate for $t = 3$:
$80t - 16t^2 = 80(3) - 16(3)^2 = 96$
Evaluate for $t = 4$:
$80t - 16t^2 = 80(4) - 16(4)^2 = 64$
Evaluate for $t = 5$:
$80t - 16t^2 = 80(5) - 16(5)^2 = 0$

Since the height of the rocket is 0 when $t = 5$, the rocket will hit the ground in 5 seconds.

The two columns of a table of values are sometimes headed with the terms **input** and **output,** as shown. The t-values are the inputs into the expression $80t - 16t^2$, and the resulting values are thought of as the outputs.

Input	Output
1	64
2	96
3	96
4	64
5	0

ANSWERS TO SELF CHECKS

1. $1, -12, 3, -4$ **2. a.** factor **b.** term **3. a.** $t - 80$ **b.** $\frac{2}{3}T$ **c.** $2a - 15$
4. $(m + 15)$ minutes **5.** $\frac{x}{2}$ hours **6.** $x =$ the number of calories in a serving of pears, $2x =$ the number of calories in a candy bar **7.** $s =$ amount donated to scholarship fund in dollars, $900 - s =$ amount donated to building fund **8.** $x =$ the number of votes received by the challenger, $3x - 55 =$ the number of votes received by the incumbent
9. Daughter's: x, Kayla's: $x + 5$, Son's: $x + 2$ **10.** $1, 2, 3, \dfrac{h}{24}$ **11. a.** \$300 **b.** \$100t
c. \$1,000$(x - 4)$ **12. a.** 2 **b.** -25 **13.** $-4°$F **14.** 7 sec (the heights are 96, 192, 160, and 0)

SECTION **4.1**   STUDY SET

VOCABULARY

Fill in the blanks.

1. To _____ an algebraic expression, we substitute the values for the variables and then apply the rules for the order of operations.

2. Variables and/or numbers can be combined with the operation symbols of addition, subtraction, multiplication, and division to create algebraic _____.

3. $2x + 5$ is an example of an algebraic _____, whereas $2x + 5 = 7$ is an example of an _____.

4. When we evaluate an algebraic expression, such as $5x - 8$, for several values of x, we can keep track of the results in an input/output _____.

CONCEPTS

5. Write two algebraic expressions that contain the variable x and the numbers 6 and 20.

6. a. Complete the table to determine how many days are in w weeks.

Number of weeks	Number of days
1	
2	
3	
w	

b. Complete the table to answer this question: *s* seconds is how many minutes?

Number of seconds	Number of minutes
60	
120	
180	
s	

7. When evaluating $3x - 6$ for $x = 4$, what misunderstanding can occur if we don't write parentheses around 4 when it is substituted for the variable?

8. If the knife shown is 12 inches long, write an expression for the length of the blade.

9. a. In the illustration, the weight of the van is 500 pounds less than twice the weight of the car. If the car weighs *x* pounds, write an expression that represents the weight of the van.

b. If the actual weight of the car is 2,000 pounds, what is the weight of the van?

10. See the illustration.

a. If we let $b =$ the length of the beam, write an expression for the length of the pipe.

b. If we let $p =$ the length of the pipe, write an expression for the length of the beam.

15 ft

11. Complete the table.

Type of coin	Number ·	Value in cents =	Total value in cents
Nickel	6		
Dime	*d*		
Half dollar	$x + 5$		

12. If $x = -9$, find the value of

a. $-x$ **b.** $-(-x)$

c. $-x^2$ **d.** $(-x)^2$

▌ NOTATION

Complete each evaluation.

13. Evaluate the expression $9a - a^2$ for $a = 5$.

$$9a - a^2 = 9\left(\;\;\right) - \left(\;\;\right)^2$$
$$= 9(5) - \boxed{}$$
$$= \boxed{} - 25$$
$$= 20$$

14. Evaluate $\dfrac{4x^2 - 3y}{9(x - y)}$ when $x = 4$ and $y = -3$.

$$\frac{4x^2 - 3}{9\left(x - \;\right)} = \frac{4(4)^2 - 3\left(\;\;\right)}{9\left[4 - \left(\;\;\right)\right]}$$

$$= \frac{4\left(\;\;\right) - 3\left(\;\;\right)}{9\left(\;\;\right)}$$

$$= \frac{\left(\;\;\right) - \left(\;\;\right)}{\boxed{}}$$

$$= \frac{73}{63}$$

▌ GUIDED PRACTICE

Identify the coefficient of each term in the expression. See Example 1.

15. $4x^2 - 5x + 7$ **16.** $-8x^2 + 3x - 2$

17. $9x^2 - 4x$ **18.** $-5x^2 + 6$

Is n used as a factor or a term in each expression? See Example 2.

19. $n - 4$ **20.** $3n - 4$

21. $-5n^2 - 4n + 3$ **22.** $5m^2 + n$

Write each phrase as an algebraic expression. If no variable is given, use x as the variable. See Example 3.

23. The sum of the length *l* and 15

24. The difference of a number and 10

25. The product of a number and 50

26. Three-fourths of the population *p*

27. The ratio of the amount won *w* and lost *l*

28. The tax *t* added to *c*

29. *P* increased by *p*

30. 21 less than the total height *h*

31. The square of *k* minus 2,005

32. *s* subtracted from *S*

33. *J* reduced by 500

34. Twice the attendance *a*

35. 1,000 split *n* equal ways

36. Exceeds the cost *c* by 25,000

37. 90 more than the current price *p*

38. 64 divided by the cube of *y*

Write an algebraic expression that represents each quantity.
See Example 4.

39. A model's skirt is *x* inches long. The designer then lets the hem down 2 inches. How can we express the length (in inches) of the altered skirt?

40. A caterer always prepares food for 10 more people than the order specifies. If *p* people are to attend a reception, write an expression for the number of people she should prepare for.

41. Last year a club sold *x* candy bars for a fundraiser. This year they want to sell 150 more than last year. Write an expression for the number of candy bars they want to sell this year.

42. The tag on a new pair of 36-inch-long jeans warns that after washing, they will shrink *x* inches in length. Express the length (in inches) of the jeans after they are washed.

Write an algebraic expression that represents each quantity.
See Example 5.

43. A soft-drink manufacturer produced *c* cans of cola during the morning shift. Write an expression for how many six-packs of cola can be assembled from the morning shift's production.

44. A student has a paper to type that contains *x* words. If the student can type 60 words per minute, write an expression for the number of minutes it will take for her to type the paper.

45. A walking path is *x* feet wide and is striped down the middle. Write an expression for the width of each lane of the path.

46. Tickets to a musical cost a total of $*t* for 5 tickets. Write an expression for the cost of one ticket to the musical.

Write an algebraic expression that represents each quantity.
See Example 6.

47. A caravan of *b* cars, each carrying 5 people, traveled to the state capital for a political rally. Express how many people were in the car caravan.

48. Tickets to a circus cost $5 each. Express how much tickets will cost for a family of *x* people if they also pay for two of their neighbors.

49. A rectangle is twice as long as it is wide. If the rectangle's width is *w*, write an expression for the length.

50. If each egg is worth *e*¢, express the value (in cents) of a dozen eggs.

Write an algebraic expression that represents each quantity.
See Examples 7–8.

51. A 12-foot board is to be cut into two pieces. Choose a variable to represent the length of one piece. Then write an expression that represents the other piece.

52. Part of a $10,000 investment is to be invested in an account paying 2% interest, and the rest in an account paying 3%. Choose a variable to represent the amount invested at 2%. Then write an expression that represents the amount invested at 3%.

53. The number of runners in a marathon this year is 25 more than twice the number that participated last year. Write an expression that represents the number of marathon runners this year.

54. In the second year of operation, a bakery sold 31 more than three times the number of cakes it sold the first year. Write an expression that represents the number of cakes the bakery sold the second year of operation.

Write an algebraic expression that represents each quantity.
See Example 9.

55. IBM was founded 80 years before Apple Computer. Dell Computer Corporation was founded 9 years after Apple.

  a. Let *x* represent the age (in years) of one of the companies. Write algebraic expressions to represent the ages (in years) of the other two companies.

  b. On April 1, 2008, Apple Computer Company was 32 years old. How old were the other two companies then?

56. Abraham Lincoln was inaugurated 60 years after Thomas Jefferson. Barack Obama was inaugurated 208 years after Jefferson. Write algebraic expressions to represent the year of inauguration of each of these presidents.

57. Florida became a state 27 years after Illinois. California became a state 32 years after Illinois. Write algebraic expressions to represent the year of statehood of each of these states.

58. Minnesota became a state 13 years after Texas. Arizona became a state 67 years after Texas. Write algebraic expressions to represent the year of statehood of each of these states.

Write an algebraic expression that represents each quantity.
See Examples 10–11.

59. How many minutes are there in
  a. 5 hours
  b. h hours?

60. A woman watches television x hours a day. Express the number of hours she watches TV
  a. in a week
  b. in a year

61. a. How many feet are in y yards?
  b. How many yards are in f feet?

62. A sales clerk earns $\$x$ an hour. How much does he earn in
  a. an 8-hour day?
  b. a 40-hour week?

Evaluate each expression, for $x = 3$, $y = -2$, and $z = -4$.
See Example 12.

63. $(3 + x)y$

64. $(4 + z)y$

65. $3y^2 - 6y - 4$

66. $-z^2 - z - 12$

67. $(4x)^2 + 3y^2$

68. $4x^2 + (3y)^2$

69. $(x + y)^2 - |z + y|$

70. $[(z - 1)(z + 1)]^2$

71. $-\dfrac{2x + y^3}{y + 2z}$

72. $-\dfrac{2z^2 - y}{2x - y^2}$

73. $\dfrac{yz + 4x}{2z + y}$

74. $\dfrac{5y + z}{z - x}$

Evaluate each formula for the given values. See Example 13.

75. $b^2 - 4ac$ for $a = -1, b = 5,$ and $c = -2$

76. $a^2 + 2ab + b^2$ for $a = -5$ and $b = -1$

77. $\dfrac{n}{2}[2a + (n - 1)d]$ for $n = 10, a = -4,$ and $d = 6$

78. $\dfrac{a(1 - r^n)}{1 - r}$ for $a = -5, r = 2,$ and $n = 3$

Complete each table. See Example 14.

79.

x	$x^3 - 1$
0	
−1	
−3	

80.

g	$g^2 - 7g + 1$
0	
7	
−10	

81.

s	$\dfrac{5s + 36}{s}$
1	
6	
−12	

82.

a	$2{,}500a + a^3$
2	
4	
−5	

83.

Input x	Output $2x - \dfrac{x}{2}$
100	
−300	

84.

Input x	Output $\dfrac{x}{3} + \dfrac{x}{4}$
12	
−36	

85.

x	$(x + 1)(x + 5)$
−1	
−5	
−6	

86.

x	$\dfrac{1}{x + 8}$
−7	
−9	
−8	

TRY IT YOURSELF

Translate each phrase into an algebraic expression.

87. The total of $35, h,$ and 300

88. x decreased by 17

89. 680 fewer than the entire population p

90. Triple the number of expected participants x

91. The product of d and 4, decreased by 15

92. Forty-five more than the quotient of y and 6

93. Twice the sum of 200 and t

94. The square of the quantity, 14 less than x

95. The absolute value of the difference of a and 2

96. The absolute value of a, decreased by 2

97. Four more than twice x

98. Five less than twice w

LOOK ALIKES . . .

Translate each phrase to mathematical symbols. Let x represent the unknown number.

99. a. The sum of a number and 7 squared
  b. The sum of a number and 7, squared

100. a. 19 less than a number
  b. 19 is less than a number

101. a. 4 times a number increased by 2
  b. 4 times a number, increased by 2

102. a. Twice a number decreased by 3
  b. Twice a number, decreased by 3

CONCEPT EXTENSIONS

103. For what values of x would the expression $2x^2 - 7$ have the value 1?

104. Translate to an expression: The sum of a number decreased by six, and seven more than the quotient of triple the number and five.

105. If a is a positive real number, which expression has the greatest value?

$$\frac{a}{2} \qquad -a^2 \qquad 2a \qquad -|2a| \qquad \frac{a}{-2} \qquad -2a$$

106. If b is a negative real number, which expression has the least value?

$$\frac{b}{-4} \qquad b^4 \qquad 4b \qquad -|4b| \qquad -4b \qquad \frac{-b}{4}$$

APPLICATIONS

107. ROCKETRY The algebraic expression $64t - 16t^2$ gives the height of a toy rocket (in feet) t seconds after being launched. Find the height of the rocket for each of the times shown in the table.

t	h
0	
1	
2	
3	
4	

108. GROWING SOD To determine the number of square feet of sod *remaining* in a field after filling an order, the manager of a sod farm uses the expression $20{,}000 - 3s$ (where s is the number of 1-foot-by-3-foot strips the customer has ordered). To sod a soccer field, a city orders 7,000 strips of sod. Evaluate the expression for this value of s and explain the result.

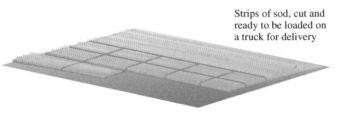

Strips of sod, cut and ready to be loaded on a truck for delivery

109. ANTIFREEZE The expression

$$\frac{5(F - 32)}{9}$$

converts a temperature in degrees Fahrenheit (given as F) to degrees Celsius. Convert the temperatures listed on the container of antifreeze in the next column to degrees Celsius. Round to the nearest degree.

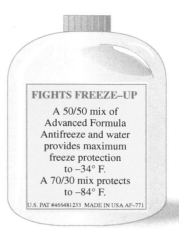

FIGHTS FREEZE–UP

A 50/50 mix of Advanced Formula Antifreeze and water provides maximum freeze protection to –34° F. A 70/30 mix protects to –84° F.

U.S. PAT #466481233 MADE IN USA AF–771

110. TEMPERATURE ON MARS On Mars, maximum summer temperatures can reach 20°C. However, daily temperatures average −33°C. Convert each of these temperatures to degrees Fahrenheit. See Example 13 (page 11). Round to the nearest degree.

111. TOOLS The utility knife blade shown is in the shape of a trapezoid. Find the area of the front face of the blade. The expression $\frac{1}{2}h(b + d)$ gives the area of a trapezoid.

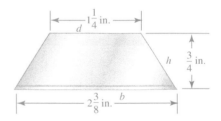

112. TRUMPET MUTES The expression

$$\pi[b^2 + d^2 + (b + d)s]$$

can be used to find the total surface area of the trumpet mute shown. Evaluate the expression for the given dimensions to find the number of square inches of cardboard (to the nearest tenth) used to make the mute.

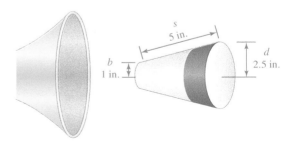

113. LANDSCAPING A grass strip is to be planted around a tree, as shown. Find the number of square feet of sod to order by evaluating the expression $\pi(R^2 - r^2)$. Round to the nearest square foot.

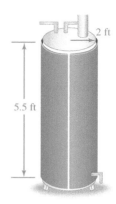

$R = 9.75$ ft $r = 4.5$ ft

114. ENERGY CONSERVATION A fiberglass blanket wrapped around a water heater helps prevent heat loss. Find the number of square feet of heater surface the blanket covers by evaluating the algebraic expression $2\pi rh$, where r is the radius and h is the height. Round to the nearest square foot.

WRITING

115. What is an algebraic expression? Give some examples.

116. What is a variable? How are variables used in this section?

117. In this section, we substituted a number for a variable. List some other uses of the word *substitute* that you encounter in everyday life.

118. Explain why d dimes are not worth d cents.

SECTION 4.2

Applications Introduction: Properties of Real Numbers

In Section 4.1, we discussed **algebraic expressions.**

Algebraic Expressions

Variables and/or numbers can be combined with the operations of addition, subtraction, multiplication, and division to create **algebraic expressions.**

In algebra, it is often helpful to replace one algebraic expression with another that is equivalent and simpler in form. That process is called **simplifying an expression.**

For example, in Section 4.2, you will learn that the expression $4x + 5x$ can be replaced with the equivalent (and simpler) expression $9x$ and the expression $9 \cdot 2y$ can be replaced with the expression $18y$. To simplify algebraic expressions such as these, we use properties of real numbers.

The **commutative properties** enable us to add or multiply two numbers in either order and obtain the same result. Here are two examples.

$$3 + (-5) = -2 \quad \text{and} \quad -5 + 3 = -2$$
$$-2.6(-8) = 20.8 \quad \text{and} \quad -8(-2.6) = 20.8$$

The **associative properties** enable us to group the numbers in an addition or multiplication any way that we wish and get the same result. For example,

$$(19 + 7) + 3 = 26 + 3 = 29 \quad \text{and} \quad 19 + (7 + 3) = 19 + 10 = 29$$
$$(4 \cdot 2)6 = 8 \cdot 6 = 48 \quad \text{and} \quad 4(2 \cdot 6) = 4 \cdot 12 = 48$$

Properties of Real Numbers

If a, b, and c represent real numbers, we have
The commutative properties of addition and multiplication

$$a + b = b + a \qquad ab = ba$$

The associative properties of addition and multiplication

$$(a + b) + c = a + (b + c) \qquad (ab)c = a(bc)$$

1. Which property of addition is shown?
   a. $3 + 4 = 4 + 3$

   b. $(3 + 4) + 5 = 3 + (4 + 5)$

   c. $(36 + 58) + 32 = 36 + (58 + 32)$

   d. $319 + 507 = 507 + 319$

2. Which property of multiplication is shown?
   a. $-2 \cdot (5 \cdot 77) = (-2 \cdot 5) \cdot 77$

   b. $28 \cdot \dfrac{1}{4} = \dfrac{1}{4} \cdot 28$

   c. $(44 \cdot 10) \cdot 0.8 = 44 \cdot (10 \cdot 0.8)$
   d. $8(47 \cdot 1) = 8(1 \cdot 47)$

3. CHECKING ACCOUNTS To find the total dollar amount of the checks entered in the register below, we could add the amounts in the order in which they are written:

$$\$39 + \$75 + 34 + \$25 + \$111 + \$16$$

Number	Date	Description of Transaction	Payment/Debit	
101	3/6	DR. OKAMOTO, DDS	$39	00
102	3/6	UNION OIL CO.	$75	00
103	3/8	STATER BROS.	$34	00
104	3/9	LITTLE LEAGUE	$25	00
105	3/11	NORDSTROM	$111	00
106	3/12	OFFICE MAX	$16	00

   a. It would be easier to add the check amounts if they were reordered and grouped differently. Fill in the blanks to make the addition easier:

$$(\$39 + \quad) + (\$75 + \quad) + (\$34 + \quad)$$
$$= \quad \$150 \quad + \quad \quad + \quad \$50$$
$$= \quad$$

   b. Which properties did you use to make the addition easier?

   Another property of real numbers that we will use in Section 4.2 to simplify algebraic expressions is the **distributive property.** One way to introduce this property is with a geometric example.

4. PARKING AREAS Refer to the illustration below.

    a. What is the length of the entire parking lot? Write an algebraic expression that represents the width of the entire parking lot. Fill in the blanks:

        The area of the entire parking lot is: ____ (____) square meters

    b. What is the length of the self parking lot? What algebraic expression represents the width of the self parking lot? Fill in the blanks:

        The area of the self parking lot is: ____ x square meters

    c. What is the length of the valet parking lot? What is its width? What is the area of the valet parking lot? (You should get a number.)

        The area of the valet parking lot is: ____ square meters

    d. Use your answers to parts a, b, and c to translate the verbal model to mathematical symbols.

The area of entire parking lot	equals	the area of self parking lot	plus	the area of valet parking lot.
_____	=	_____	+	_____

Length 20 meters

VALET PARKING — 6 meters

SELF PARKING — x meters

Problem 4 is an example of the use of the *distributive property*.

The Distributive Property of Multiplication Over Addition

If a, b, and c represent real numbers,

$$a(b + c) = ab + ac$$

To explain the distributive property in more detail, detail, let's consider the expression $5(x + 3)$. Since we are not given the value of x, we cannot add x and 3 within the parentheses. However, we can distribute the multiplication by the factor of 5 that is outside the parentheses to x and to 3 and add those products.

$$5(x + 3) = 5(x) + 5(3) \qquad \text{Distribute the multiplication by 5.}$$
$$= 5x + 15 \qquad \text{Do the multiplication.}$$

5. The distributive property can also be demonstrated using the following illustration.

    a. Fill in the blanks: Two groups of 6 plus three groups of 6 is ⬚ groups of 6.

      Therefore,

$$\boxed{} \cdot 2 + \boxed{} \cdot 3 = 6(\boxed{} + \boxed{})$$

    b. Draw a diagram that illustrates

$$5 \cdot 4 + 5 \cdot 6 = 5(4 + 6).$$

SECTION 4.2

Simplifying Algebraic Expressions Using Properties of Real Numbers

Objectives

1 Use the commutative and associative properties.

2 Simplify products.

3 Use the distributive property.

4 Identify like terms.

5 Combine like terms.

ARE YOU READY?

The following problems review some basic concepts that are important when simplifying expressions using properties of real numbers.

1. How do the expressions $3 + x$ and $x + 3$ differ?

2. How do the expressions $1 + (7 + x)$ and $(1 + 7) + x$ differ?

3. Evaluate $5(2 + 4)$ and $5 \cdot 2 + 5 \cdot 4$ and compare the results.

4. How do the terms $4x$ and $4y$ differ? What do they have in common?

In algebra, we often replace one algebraic expression with another that is equivalent and simpler in form. That process, called *simplifying an algebraic expression,* often involves the use of one or more properties of real numbers.

1 **Use the Commutative and Associative Properties.**

Recall the commutative and associative properties discussed in Sections 1.4 and 1.6.

Commutative Properties

Changing the order when adding or multiplying does not affect the answer.

$$a + b = b + a \qquad \text{and} \qquad ab = ba$$

> ## Associative Properties
>
> Changing the grouping when adding or multiplying does not affect the answer.
>
> $$(a + b) + c = a + (b + c) \quad \text{and} \quad (ab)c = a(bc)$$

These properties can be applied when working with algebraic expressions that involve addition and multiplication.

Self Check 1

Use the given property to complete each statement.

a. $5x + (3x + 1) =$

   Associative property of addition

b. $a(-15) =$ Commutative property of multiplication

Now Try **Problem 19 and 21**

EXAMPLE 1   Use the given property to complete each statement.

a. $9 + x =$ _____   Commutative property of addition

b. $t \cdot 5 =$ _____   Commutative property of multiplication

c. $(a + 92) + 8 =$ _____   Associative property of addition

d. $6(10n) =$ _____   Associative property of multiplication

Strategy For problems like these, it is important to memorize the properties by name. To fill in each blank, we will determine the way in which the property enables us to rewrite the given expression.

WHY We should memorize the properties by name because their names remind us how to use them.

Solution

a. To *commute* means to go back and forth. The commutative property of addition enables us to change the order of the terms, 9 and x.

$9 + x = \underline{x + 9}$ Commutative property of addition

b. We change the order of the factors, t and 5.

$t \cdot 5 = \underline{5 \cdot t}$ Commutative property of multiplication

c. To *associate* means to group together. The associative property of addition enables us to group the terms in a different way.

$(a + 92) + 8 = \underline{a + (92 + 8)}$ Associative property of addition

d. We change the grouping of the factors, 6, 10, and n.

$6(10n) = \underline{(6 \cdot 10)n}$ Associative property of multiplication

2 Simplify products.

The commutative and associative properties of multiplication can be used to simplify certain products. As an example, let's consider the expression $8(4x)$ and simplify it as follows:

$$8(4x) = 8 \cdot (4 \cdot x) \quad \text{\small } 4x = 4 \cdot x$$
$$= (8 \cdot 4) \cdot x \quad \text{\small Use the associative property of multiplication to group 4 with 8 instead of with x.}$$
$$= 32x \quad \text{\small Perform the multiplication within the parentheses: } 8 \cdot 4 = 32.$$

Since $8(4x) = 32x$, we say that $8(4x)$ simplifies to $32x$. To verify that $8(4x)$ and $32x$ are **equivalent expressions** (represent the same number), we can evaluate each expression for several choices of x. For each value of x, the results should be the same.

If $x = 10$		If $x = -3$	
$8(4x) = 8[4(10)]$	$32x = 32(10)$	$8(4x) = 8[4(-3)]$	$32x = 32(-3)$
$= 8(40)$	$= 320$	$= 8(-12)$	$= -96$
$= 320$		$= -96$	

EXAMPLE 2 Simplify each expression:

a. $15a(-7)$ **b.** $5\left(\frac{4}{5}x\right)$ **c.** $-5r(-6s)$ **d.** $3(7p)(-5p)$

Strategy We will use the commutative and associative properties of multiplication to reorder and regroup the factors.

WHY We want to group the numerical factors of the expression together so that we can find their product.

Solution

a. $15a(-7) = 15(-7)a$ Use the commutative property of multiplication to change the order of the factors.

$= -105a$ Working left to right, perform the multiplications.

b. $5\left(\frac{4}{5}x\right) = \left(5 \cdot \frac{4}{5}\right)x$ Use the associative property of multiplication to group the numbers.

$= 4x$ Multiply: $5 \cdot \frac{4}{5} = \frac{5}{1} \cdot \frac{4}{5} = \frac{\overset{1}{\cancel{5}} \cdot 4}{1 \cdot \cancel{5}} = 4.$

c. We note that the expression contains two variables.

$-5r(-6s) = [-5(-6)][r \cdot s]$ Use the commutative and associative properties of multiplication to group the numbers and group the variables.

$= 30rs$ Perform the multiplications within the brackets: $-5(-6) = 30$ and $r \cdot s = rs$.

d. $3(7p)(-5p) = [3(7)(-5)](p \cdot p)$ Use the commutative and associative properties of multiplication to change the order and to regroup the factors.

$= -105p^2$ Perform the multiplication within the grouping symbols: $3(7)(-5) = -105$ and $p \cdot p = p^2$.

Self Check 2

Simplify each expression:

a. $9 \cdot 6s$ **b.** $8\left(\frac{7}{8}h\right)$

c. $21p(-3q)$ **d.** $-4(6m)(-2m)$

Now Try **Problem 33**

> **Success Tip** By the commutative property of multiplication, we can change the order of the factors.

---

3 Use the distributive property.

To introduce the **distributive property,** we will consider the expression $4(5 + 3)$, which can be evaluated in two ways.

Method 1. Rules for the order of operations: We compute the sum within the parentheses first.

$4(5 + 3) = 4(8)$ Perform the addition within the parentheses first.

$= 32$ Perform the multiplication.

Method 2. The distributive property: We multiply both 5 and 3 by 4, and then we add the results.

$$4(5 + 3) = 4(5) + 4(3) \qquad \text{Distribute the multiplication by 4.}$$
$$= 20 + 12 \qquad \text{Perform the multiplications.}$$
$$= 32 \qquad \text{Perform the addition.}$$

Notice that each method gives a result of 32.

We can interpret the distributive property geometrically. The figure below shows three rectangles that are divided into squares. Since the area of the rectangle on the left-hand side of the equals sign can be found by multiplying its width by its length, its area is $4(5 + 3)$ square units. We can evaluate this expression, or we can count squares; either way, we see that the area is 32 square units.

The area shown on the right-hand side is the sum of the areas of two rectangles: $4(5) + 4(3)$. Either by evaluating this expression or by counting squares, we see that this area is also 32 square units. Therefore,

$$4(5 + 3) = 4(5) + 4(3)$$

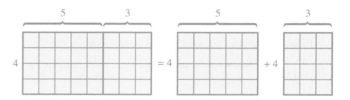

The following figure shows the general case where the width is a and the length is $b + c$.

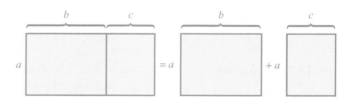

Using the figure as a basis, we can now state the distributive property in symbols.

The Distributive Property

For any real numbers, a, b, and c,

$$a(b + c) = ab + ac$$

Since subtraction is the same as adding the opposite, the distributive property also holds for subtraction.

The Distributive Property

For any real numbers, a, b, and c,

$$a(b - c) = ab - ac$$

To illustrate one use of the distributive property, let's consider the expression $5(x + 2)$. Since we are not given the value of x, we cannot add x and 2 within the parentheses. However, we can distribute the multiplication by the factor of 5 that is outside the parentheses to x and to 2 and add those products.

$$5(x + 2) = 5(x) + 5(2) \qquad \text{Distribute the multiplication by 5.}$$
$$= 5x + 10 \qquad \text{Perform the multiplications.}$$

Caution!   Since the expression $5(x + 2)$ contains parentheses, some students are tempted to perform the addition within the parentheses first. However, we cannot add x and 2, because we do not know the value of x. Instead, we should multiply $x + 2$ by 5, which requires the use of the distributive property.

EXAMPLE 3   Multiply: **a.** $3(x - 8)$ **b.** $-12(a + 1)$ **c.** $-6(-3y - 8)$

Strategy We will use the distributive property to multiply each term within the parentheses by the factor outside the parentheses.

WHY In each case, we cannot simplify the expression within the parentheses.

Solution

a. $3(x - 8) = 3(x) - 3(8)$ Distribute the multiplication by 3.

$\qquad\qquad = 3x - 24$ Perform the multiplications.

b. $-12(a + 1) = -12(a) + (-12)(1)$ Distribute the multiplication by -12.

$\qquad\qquad\qquad = -12a + (-12)$ Perform the multiplications.

$\qquad\qquad\qquad = -12a - 12$ Write the addition of -12 as subtraction of 12.

c. $-6(-3y - 8) = -6(-3y) - (-6)(8)$ Distribute the multiplication by -6.

$\qquad\qquad\qquad = 18y - (-48)$ Perform the multiplications.

$\qquad\qquad\qquad = 18y + 48$ Add the opposite of -48, which is 48.

Caution!   A common mistake is to forget to distribute the multiplication over each of the terms within the parentheses.

$$3(3b - 4) = 9b - 4$$

Caution!   The fact that an expression contains parentheses does not necessarily mean that the distributive property can be applied. For example, the distributive property does not apply to the expressions:

$6(5x)$ or $6(-7 \cdot y)$ Here a product is multiplied by 6. Simplifying, we have $6(5x) = 30x$ and $6(-7 \cdot y) = -42y$.

However, the distributive property does apply to the expressions:

$6(5 + x)$ or $6(-7 - y)$ Here a sum and a difference are multiplied by 6. Distributing the 6, we have $6(5 + x) = 30 + 6x$ and $6(-7 - y) = -42 - 6y$.

Self Check 3

Multiply:
a. $5(p + 2)$
b. $4(t - 1)$
c. $-8(2x - 4)$

Now Try **Problem 39**

To use the distributive property to simplify $-(x + 10)$, we note that the negative sign in front of the parentheses represents -1.

The $-$ sign represents -1.

$$-(x + 10) = -1(x + 10)$$
$$= -1(x) + (-1)(10) \quad \text{Distribute the multiplication by } -1.$$
$$= -x + (-10) \quad \text{Multiply: } -1(x) = -x \text{ and } (-1)(10) = -10.$$
$$= -x - 10 \quad \text{Write the addition of } -10 \text{ as a subtraction.}$$

Self Check 4
Simplify: $-(-5x + 18)$
Now Try **Problem 49**

EXAMPLE 4   Simplify: $-(-12 - 3p)$

Strategy We will use the distributive property to multiply each term within the parentheses by -1.

WHY The "$-$" symbol outside the parentheses represents a factor of -1.

Solution
$$-(-12 - 3p)$$
$$= -1(-12 - 3p) \quad \text{Change the } - \text{ sign in front of the parentheses to } -1.$$
$$= -1(-12) - (-1)(3p) \quad \text{Distribute the multiplication by } -1.$$
$$= 12 - (-3p) \quad \text{Multiply: } -1(-12) = 12 \text{ and } (-1)(3p) = -3p.$$
$$= 12 + 3p \quad \text{To subtract } -3p, \text{ add the opposite of } -3p, \text{ which is } 3p.$$

Success Tip   Notice that distributing the multiplication by -1 changes the sign of each term within the parentheses.

Since multiplication is commutative, we can write the distributive property in the following forms.

$$(b + c)a = ba + ca \qquad (b - c)a = ba - ca$$

Self Check 5
Multiply: $(-6x - 24y)\dfrac{1}{3}$
Now Try **Problem 54**

EXAMPLE 5   Multiply: $(6x + 4y)\dfrac{1}{2}$

Strategy We will use the distributive property to multiply each term within the parentheses by the factor outside the parentheses.

WHY In each case, we cannot simplify the expression within the parentheses.

Solution

$$(6x + 4y)\frac{1}{2} = (6x)\frac{1}{2} + (4y)\frac{1}{2} \quad \text{Distribute the multiplication by } \tfrac{1}{2}.$$
$$= 3x + 2y \quad \text{Multiply: } (6x)\tfrac{1}{2} = \left(6 \cdot \tfrac{1}{2}\right)x = 3x \text{ and } (4y)\tfrac{1}{2} = \left(4 \cdot \tfrac{1}{2}\right)y = 2y.$$

The distributive property can be extended to situations in which there are more than two terms within parentheses.

The Extended Distributive Property

For any real numbers, $a, b,$ and $c,$

$$a(b + c + d) = ab + ac + ad \quad \text{and} \quad a(b - c - d) = ab - ac - ad$$

EXAMPLE 6   Multiply: $-0.3(3a - 4b + 7)$

Strategy We will use the distributive property to multiply each term within the parentheses by the factor outside the parentheses.

WHY We cannot simplify the expression within the parentheses.

Solution

$-0.3(3a - 4b + 7)$

$$= -0.3(3a) - (-0.3)(4b) + (-0.3)(7) \qquad \text{Distribute the multiplication by } -0.3.$$

$$= -0.9a - (-1.2b) + (-2.1) \qquad \text{Perform the three multiplications.}$$

$$= -0.9a + 1.2b + (-2.1) \qquad \text{To subtract } -1.2b, \text{ add its opposite, which is } 1.2b.$$

$$= -0.9a + 1.2b - 2.1 \qquad \text{Write the addition of } -2.1 \text{ as a subtraction.}$$

Self Check 6

Multiply: $-0.7(2r + 5s - 8)$

Now Try **Problem 57**

4 Identify like terms.

The expression $5p + 7q - 3p + 12$, which can be written $5p + 7q + (-3p) + 12$, contains four terms, $5p$, $7q$, $-3p$, and 12. Since the variable of $5p$ and $-3p$ are the same, we say that these terms are **like** or **similar terms.**

Like Terms (Similar Terms)

Like terms (or **similar terms**) are terms with exactly the same variables raised to exactly the same powers. Any numbers (called **constants**) in an expression are considered to be like terms.

Like terms	**Unlike terms**
$4x$ and $7x$	$4x$ and $3y$
↓ ↓	↓ ↓
Same variable	Different variables
$-10p^2$, $25p^2$, and $150p^2$	$15p$ and $23p^2$
Same variable to the same power	Different exponents on the variable p

---

Caution! It is important to be able to distinguish between a *term* of an expression and a *factor* of a term. Terms are separated by + symbols. Factors are numbers and/or variables that are multiplied together. For example, x is a term of the expression $18 + x$, because x and 18 are separated by a + symbol. In the expression $18x + 9$, x is a factor of the term $18x$, because x and 18 are multiplied together.

EXAMPLE 7   List like terms:

a. $7r + 5 + 3r$ **b.** $x^4 - 6x^2 - 5$ **c.** $-7m + 7 - 2 + m$

Strategy First we will identify each term of the expression. Then we will look for terms that contain the same variable factors raised to exactly the same powers.

WHY If terms contain the same variables raised to the same powers, they are like terms.

Self Check 7

List like terms:
a. $5x - 2y + 7y$
b. $-5pq + 17p - 12q - 2pq$

Now Try **Problem 59**

Solution

a. $7r + 5 + 3r$ contains the like terms $7r$ and $3r$.

b. $x^4 - 6x^2 - 5$ contains no like terms.

c. $-7m + 7 - 2 + m$ contains two pairs of like terms: $-7m$ and m are like terms, and the constants, 7 and -2, are like terms.

5 Combine like terms.

To add (or subtract) objects, they must have the same units. For example, we can add dollars to dollars and inches to inches, but we cannot add dollars to inches. The same is true when we work with terms of an algebraic expression. They can be added or subtracted only when they are like terms.

This expression can be simplified, because it contains like terms.

$$3x + 4x$$

Like terms
The variable parts are identical.

This expression cannot be simplified, because its terms are not like terms.

$$3x + 4y$$

Unlike terms
The variable parts are not identical.

To simplify an expression containing like terms, we use the distributive property. For example, we can simplify $3x + 4x$ as follows:

$$3x + 4x = (3 + 4)x \quad \text{Use the distributive property.}$$
$$= 7x \quad \text{Perform the addition within the parentheses: } 3 + 4 = 7.$$

We have simplified the expression $3x + 4x$ by **combining like terms.** The result is the equivalent expression $7x$. This example suggests the following general rule.

> ### Combining Like Terms
>
> To add or subtract like terms, combine their coefficients and keep the same variables with the same exponents.

Self Check 8

Simplify by combining like terms:
a. $5n + (-8n)$
b. $-1.2a^3 + 1.4a^3$

Now Try **Problem 65**

EXAMPLE 8   Simplify by combining like terms:
a. $-8p + (-12p)$ **b.** $0.5s^2 - 0.3s^2$

Strategy We will use the distributive property in reverse to add (or subtract) the coefficients of the like terms. We will keep the variable factors raised to the same powers.

WHY To *combine like terms* means to add or subtract the like terms in an expression.

Solution

a. $-8p + (-12p) = -20p$ Add the coefficients of the like terms:
$-8 + (-12) = -20.$ Keep the variable p.

b. $0.5s^2 - 0.3s^2 = 0.2s^2$ Subtract: $0.5 - 0.3 = 0.2.$ Keep the variable part s^2.

EXAMPLE 9   Simplify: $7P - 8p - 12P + 25p$

Strategy We will use the commutative property of addition to write the like terms next to each other. Keep in mind that an uppercase P and a lower case p are different variables.

WHY To *simplify* an expression we use properties of real numbers to write an equivalent expression in simpler form.

Solution

The uppercase P and the lowercase p are different variables. We can use the commutative property of addition to write like terms next to each other.

$7P - 8p - 12P + 25p$

$\quad = 7P + (-8p) + (-12P) + 25p$ Rewrite each subtraction as the addition of the opposite.

$\quad = 7P + (-12P) + (-8p) + 25p$ Use the commutative property of addition to write the like terms together.

$\quad = -5P + 17p$ Combine like terms: $7P + (-12P) = -5P$ and $-8p + 25p = 17p$. ∎

Self Check 9

Simplify: $8R + 7r - 14R - 21r$

Now Try Problem 71

The expression in Example 9 contained two sets of like terms, and we rearranged the terms so that like terms were next to each other. With practice, you will be able to combine like terms without having to write them next to each other.

EXAMPLE 10   Simplify: $4(x + 5) - 3(2x - 4)$

Strategy First we will use the distributive property to remove the parentheses. Then we will identify any like terms and combine them.

WHY To *simplify* an expression we use properties of real numbers, such as the distributive property, to write an equivalent expression in simpler form.

Solution

$4(x + 5) - 3(2x - 4)$

$\quad = 4x + 20 - 6x + 12$ Use the distributive property twice.

$\quad = -2x + 32$ Combine like terms: $4x - 6x = -2x$ and $20 + 12 = 32$. ∎

Self Check 10

Simplify: $-5(y - 4) + 2(4y + 6)$

Now Try Problem 83

ANSWERS TO SELF CHECKS

1. a. $(5x + 3x) + 1$ **b.** $-15a$ **2. a.** $54s$ **b.** $7h$ **c.** $-63pq$ **d.** $48m^2$
3. a. $5p + 10$ **b.** $4t - 4$ **c.** $-16x + 32$ **4.** $5x - 18$ **5.** $-2x - 8y$
6. $-1.4r - 3.5s + 5.6$ **7. a.** $-2y$ and $7y$ **b.** $-5pq$ and $-2pq$ **8. a.** $-3n$
b. $0.2a^3$ **9.** $-6R - 14r$ **10.** $3y + 32$

SECTION 4.2 STUDY SET

VOCABULARY

Fill in the blanks.

1. To _____ the expression $5(6x)$ means to write it in the simpler form $5(6x) = 30x$.

2. $5(6x)$ and $30x$ are _____ expressions because for each value of x, they represent the same number.

3. To perform the multiplication $2(x + 8)$, we use the _____ property to remove parentheses.

4. Terms such as $7x^2$ and $5x^2$, which have the same variables raised to exactly the same powers, are called _____ terms.

5. a. Fill in the blanks to simplify the expression.
$$4(9)t = (\quad \cdot \quad)t = \quad t$$

b. What property did you use in part a?

6. a. Fill in the blanks to simplify the expression.
$$-6y \cdot 2 = \quad \cdot \quad \cdot y = \quad y$$

b. What property did you use in part a?

CONCEPTS

7. What property does the equation $a(b + c) = ab + ac$ illustrate?

8. The illustration shows an application of the distributive property. Fill in the blanks.

$$2\left(\,\boxed{} + \boxed{}\right) = 2\left(\,\boxed{}\right) + 2\left(\,\boxed{}\right)$$

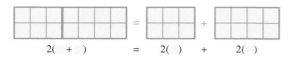

2(+)	=	2( ) + 2( )

Fill in the blanks.

9. $a(b + c + d) = \underline{\hspace{1.5in}}$

10. **a.** $2(x + 4) = 2x \;\boxed{}\; 8$

    b. $2(x - 4) = 2x \;\boxed{}\; 8$

    c. $2(-x + 4) = -2x \;\boxed{}\; 8$

    d. $2(-x - 4) = -2x \;\boxed{}\; 8$

11. **a.** $-2(x + 4) = -2x \;\boxed{}\; 8$

    b. $-2(x - 4) = -2x \;\boxed{}\; 8$

    c. $-2(-x + 4) = 2x \;\boxed{}\; 8$

    d. $-2(-x - 4) = 2x \;\boxed{}\; 8$

12. To add or subtract like terms, combine their _____ and keep the same variables and _____.

NOTATION

Complete each step

13. $7(a + 2) = \boxed{} \cdot a + \boxed{} \cdot 2$

$$= 7a + \boxed{}$$

14. $6(b - 5) + 12b + 7 = 6\left(\,\boxed{}\right) - 6\left(\,\boxed{}\right) + 12b + 7$

$$= 6b - \boxed{} + 12b + 7$$

$$= 6b + \boxed{}\, b - \boxed{} + 7$$

$$= \boxed{}\, b - 23$$

15. **a.** Are $2K$ and $3k$ like terms?

    b. Are $-d$ and d like terms?

16. Fill in the blank: $-(x + 10) = -\boxed{}\,(x + 10)$

17. Write each expression using fewer symbols.

    a. $5x - (-1)$ **b.** $16t + (-6)$

18. In the table below a student's answers to five problems are compared to the answers in the back of the book. Are the answers equivalent?

Student's answer	Book's answer	Equivalent?
$10x$	$10 + x$	
$3 + y$	$y + 3$	
$5 - 8a$	$8a - 5$	
$3(x) + 4$	$3(x + 4)$	
$2x$	x^2	

GUIDED PRACTICE

Use the given property to complete each statement. **See Example 1.**

19. $8 + (7 + a) = \underline{\hspace{1in}}$ Associative property of addition

20. $-2(5b) = \underline{\hspace{0.8in}}$ Associative property of multiplication

21. $y \cdot 11 = \underline{\hspace{0.5in}}$ Commutative property of multiplication

22. $x + x^2 = \underline{\hspace{0.7in}}$ Commutative property of addition

23. $(8d \cdot 2)6 = \underline{\hspace{0.8in}}$ Associative property of multiplication

24. $(-1 + 3a) + 7a = \underline{\hspace{1in}}$ Associative property of addition

25. $9t + (4 + t) = 9t + (\underline{\hspace{0.4in}})$ Commutative property of addition

26. $(x - 2)3 = \underline{\hspace{0.8in}}$ Commutative property of multiplication

Simplify each expression. **See Example 2.**

27. $9(7m)$ **28.** $12n(8)$

29. $5(-7q)$ **30.** $-7(5t)$

31. $12\left(\dfrac{5}{12}x\right)$ **32.** $15\left(-\dfrac{4}{15}w\right)$

33. $(-5p)(-4b)$ **34.** $(-7d)(-7c)$

35. $-5(4r)(-2r)$ **36.** $7t(-4t)(-2)$

37. $8q(-2q)(-3)$ **38.** $-3m(-5m)(-2m)$

Multiply. **See Example 3.**

39. $5(x + 3)$ **40.** $4(x + 2)$

41. $-2(b - 1)$ **42.** $-7(p - 5)$

43. $8(3t - 2)$ **44.** $9(2q + 1)$

45. $3(-5t - 4)$ **46.** $2(5x - 4)$

Multiply. **See Example 4.**

47. $-(r - 10)$ **48.** $-(h + 4)$

49. $-(x - 7)$ **50.** $-(y + 1)$

Multiply. **See Example 5.**

51. $(3w - 6)\left(-\dfrac{2}{3}\right)$ **52.** $(2y - 8)\dfrac{1}{2}$

53. $(9x - 3y)\dfrac{2}{3}$ **54.** $(4p + 3q)\dfrac{3}{4}$

Multiply. **See Example 6.**

55. $17(2x - y + 2)$ **56.** $-12(3a + 2b - 1)$

57. $-0.1(-14 + 3p - t)$ **58.** $-1.5(-x - y + 5)$

List all like terms, if any. See Example 7.

59. $8p + 7 - 5p$

60. $-7m - 3m + 5m$

61. $a^4 + 5a^2 - 7$

62. $6q^2 + 3q - 5q^2 - 2q$

Simplify each expression by combining like terms. See Example 8.

63. $3x + 17x$

64. $12y - 15y$

65. $8x^2 - 5x^2$

66. $17x^2 + 3x^2$

67. $-4x + 4x$

68. $-16y + 16y$

69. $-7b + 7b$

70. $-2c + 2c$

Simplify each expression by combining like terms. See Example 9.

71. $1.8h - 0.7h + p - 3p$

72. $-5.7m + 4.3m + 3n - 1.2n$

73. $a + a + b$

74. $-t - t - T - T$

75. $3x + 5x - 7x + 3y$

76. $-x + 3y + 2y$

77. $-13x^2 + 2x^2 - 5y^2 + 2y^2$

78. $-8x^3 - x^3 + 3y + 5y$

Simplify each expression by combining like terms. See Example 10.

79. $(a + 2) - (a - b)$

80. $3z + 2(Z - z) + Z$

81. $5(x + 3) - 3x$

82. $2x + 7(x - 3)$

83. $-(c + 7) - 2(c - 3)$

84. $-(z + 2) + 5(3 - z)$

85. $-(c - 6) + 3(c + 1)$

86. $-2(m - 1) - 4(-2 + m)$

TRY IT YOURSELF

Simplify.

87. $0.4(x - 4)$

88. $-2.2(2q + 1)$

89. $2x + 4(X - x) + 3X$

90. $3p - 6(p + z) + p$

91. $0 - 3x$

92. $0 - 4a$

93. $0 - (-t)$

94. $0 - (-2y)$

95. $\dfrac{3}{5}t + \dfrac{1}{5}t$

96. $\dfrac{3}{16}x - \dfrac{5}{16}x$

97. $(2y - 1)6$

98. $(3w - 5)5$

99. $3(y - 3) + 4(y + 1)$

100. $-5(a - 2) - 4(a + 1)$

101. $8\left(\dfrac{3}{4}y\right)$

102. $27\left(\dfrac{2}{3}x\right)$

103. $-0.2r - (-0.6r)$

104. $-1.1m - (-2.4m)$

105. $2z + 5(z - 3)$

106. $12(m + 11) - 11$

107. $6 - 4(-3c - 7)$

108. $10 - 5(-5g - 1)$

109. $-4(-6)(-4m)$

110. $-5(-9)(-4n)$

111. $-4x + 4x$

112. $-16y + 16y$

113. $36\left(\dfrac{2}{9}x - \dfrac{3}{4}\right) + 36\left(\dfrac{1}{2}\right)$

114. $40\left(\dfrac{3}{8}y - \dfrac{1}{4}\right) + 40\left(\dfrac{4}{5}\right)$

115. $4a + 4b + 4c$

116. $2x + 2y + 2z$

117. $a^3 + 2a^2 + 4a - 2a^2 - 4a - 8$

118. $c^3 - 3c^2 + 9c + 3c^2 - 9c + 27$

LOOK ALIKES...

119. a. $5(2x)$ **b.** $5 + 2x$

120. a. $6(-7x)$ **b.** $6 - 7x$

121. a. $2(3x)(3)$ **b.** $2 + 3x + 3$

122. a. $-3(2x)(4)$ **b.** $5 - 3x + 2$

123. a. $12(8n)5$ **b.** $12(8n + 5)$

124. a. $-3(-4t)(-2)$ **b.** $-3(-4t) - 2$

125. a. $6a + 6a + 6a$ **b.** $6a + 6b + 6c$

126. a. $9x - 2(-3x + 4)$ **b.** $9x - 2(-3x) + 4$

CONCEPT EXTENSIONS

127. Fill in the blanks: $-17(\quad - \quad) = -187x + 119$

128. Fill in the blanks:

$\quad(0.005x + 0.02y - 0.0003z) = 50x + 200y - 3z$

129. Fill in the blanks: $\quad\left(\dfrac{x}{54} - \dfrac{1}{42}\right) = 7x - 9$

130. Simplify: $\dfrac{x}{2} + \dfrac{x}{3} + \dfrac{x}{4} + \dfrac{x}{5} + \dfrac{x}{6}$

131. CARPENTRY A board was cut into two pieces, as shown. Add the lengths of the two pieces. How long was the original board?

x ft $(20 - x)$ ft

132. VACATIONS Let x = the number of miles driven on the first day of a 2-day driving trip. Translate the verbal model to mathematical symbols, and simplify by combining like terms.

| The miles driven one day | plus | 100 miles more than the miles driven on day 1. |

133. GEOMETRY Two angles are called **complementary angles** when the sum of their measures is 90°. Add the measures of the angles in illustration (a). Are they complementary angles?

134. GEOMETRY Two angles are called **supplementary angles** if the sum of their measures is 180°. Add the measures of the angles in illustration (b). Are they supplementary angles?

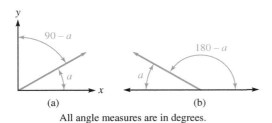

(a)   (b)

All angle measures are in degrees.

APPLICATIONS

135. THE AMERICAN RED CROSS In 1891, Clara Barton founded the Red Cross. Its symbol is a white flag bearing a red cross. If each side of the cross in the illustration has length x, write an algebraic expression for the perimeter (the total distance around the outside) of the cross.

136. BILLIARDS Billiard tables vary in size, but all tables are twice as long as they are wide.

a. If the following billiard table is x feet wide, write an expression involving x that represents its length.

b. Write an expression for the perimeter of the table.

x ft

137. PING-PONG Write an expression for the perimeter of the table shown in the illustration.

x ft $(x + 4)$ ft

138. SEWING Write an expression for the length of the blue trim needed to outline a pennant with the given side lengths.

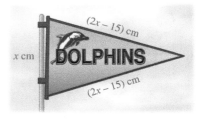

x cm $(2x - 15)$ cm $(2x - 15)$ cm

139. Use each of the words *commute*, *associate*, and *distribute* in a sentence in which the context is nonmathematical.

140. Explain each error. Then give the correct answer.

  a. $9(4b - 2) = 36b - 2$ **b.** $3(2x) = 6 \cdot 3x = 18x$

  c. $-(23c + 2) = -23c + 2$ **d.** $(5n + 1)2 = 5n + 2$

WRITING

141. Explain why the distributive property applies to $2(3 + x)$ but not to $2(3x)$.

142. Explain why $3x^2y$ and $5x^2y$ are like terms, and explain why $3x^2y$ and $5xy^2$ are not like terms.

143. Distinguish between a *factor* and a *term* of an algebraic expression. Give examples.

144. Describe how to combine like terms.

SECTION **4.3**
Applications Introduction: Properties of Equality

In Section 4.3, we will focus on *equations*. An **equation** is a mathematical statement that two algebraic expressions are equal. All equations contain an = symbol. The = symbol separates the equation into two parts: the **left side** and the **right side.** Some examples of equations are:

$$5 = 5 \quad x + 7 = 10 \quad 2y - 1 = -15 \quad 7(n + 6) = 8(n - 1) + 15$$

An equation is like a scale because it shows that the left side and the right side are in balance. In Section 4.3, it will be necessary to perform operations on the left and right sides of equations. It is important that in doing so we maintain the balance. That is, the left and right sides must remain equal. A scale is helpful in picturing this concept.

1. a. The equation 5 = 5 is represented by the illustration below.

   b. Complete the illustration below to show the result if two weights are removed from the left side of the scale in part a.

   c. Complete the illustration below to show the result if two weights are then removed from the right side of the scale in part b.

   d. Use the results of parts b and c to make a conclusion about this process in general. If the _____ amount of weight is subtracted from both sides of a balanced scale, the scale will remain in balance.

2. a. The equation 3 = 3 is represented by the illustration below.

   b. Complete the illustration below to show the result if four weights are added to the left side of the scale in part a.

c. Complete the illustration below to show the result if four weights are then added to the right side of the scale in part b.

d. Use the results of parts b and c to make a conclusion about the process in general. If the _____ amount of weight is added to both sides of a balanced scale, the scale will remain in balance

3. a. The equation 2 = 2 is represented by the illustration below.

b. Complete the illustration below to show the result if the amount of weight on the left side of the scale in part a is tripled.

c. Complete the illustration below to show the result if the amount of weight on the right side of the scale in part b is also tripled.

d. Use the results of parts b and c to make a conclusion about the process. If the amount of weight on side of a balanced scale is multiplied by the _____ factor, the scale will remain in balance.

4. a. Represent the equation 6 = 6 on the illustration below.

b. Complete the illustration in part a to show the result if the amount of weight on the left side of the scale in part a is halved.

c. Complete the illustration below to show the result if the amount of weight on the right side of the scale in part b is also halved.

d. Use the results of parts c and d to make a conclusion about the process. If the amount of weight on each side of a balanced scale is divided in the _____ way, the scale will remain in balance.

   Problems 1 through 4 are practical illustrations of some important properties that we will use in Section 4.3 when working with equations called **properties of equality.**

SECTION **4.3**
Solving Equations Using Properties of Equality

ARE YOU READY?

▼ *The following problems review some basic skills that are needed when solving equations. Fill in the blanks.*

1. $8 \quad \boxed{} \quad 8 = 0$

2. $-1.6 \quad \boxed{} \quad 1.6 = 0$

3. Evaluate $\dfrac{7}{\boxed{}} = 1$

4. $3 \quad \boxed{} \quad \dfrac{1}{3} = 1$

5. $\dfrac{2}{5} - \boxed{} = 0$

6. $-\dfrac{9}{8}\left(\boxed{} \right) = 1$

In this section, we introduce four fundamental properties of equality that are used to solve equations.

1 Determine whether a number is a solution.

An **equation** is a statement indicating that two algebraic expressions are equal. An example is $x + 5 = 15$. The equal symbol $=$ separates the equation into two parts: The expression $x + 5$ is the **left side** and 15 is the **right side.** The letter x is the **variable** (or the **unknown**). The sides of an equation can be reversed, so we can write $x + 5 = 15$ or $15 = x + 5$.

- An equation can be true: $6 + 3 = 9$
- An equation can be false: $2 + 4 = 7$
- An equation can be neither true nor false. For example, $x + 5 = 15$ is neither true nor false because we don't know what number x represents.

   An equation that contains a variable is made true or false by substituting a number for the variable. If we substitute 10 for x in $x + 5 = 15$, the resulting equation is true: $10 + 5 = 15$. If we substitute 1 for x, the resulting equation is false: $1 + 5 = 15$. A number that makes an equation true when substituted for the variable is called a **solution** and it is said to **satisfy** the equation. Therefore, 10 is a solution of $x + 5 = 15$, and 1 is not. The **solution set** of an equation is the set of all numbers that make the equation true.

> ***The Language of Algebra*** It is important to know the difference between an equation and an expression. An equation contains an = symbol and an expression does not.

Self Check 1

Is 25 a solution of
$10 - x = 35 - 2x$?

Now Try **Problem 19**

EXAMPLE 1   Is 9 a solution of $3y - 1 = 2y + 7$?

Strategy We will substitute 9 for each y in the equation and evaluate the expression on the left side and the expression on the right side separately.

WHY If a true statement results, 9 is a solution of the equation. If we obtain a false statement, 9 is not a solution.

Solution

$$3y - 1 = 2y + 7$$
$$3(9) - 1 \overset{?}{=} 2(9) + 7$$
$$27 - 1 \overset{?}{=} 18 + 7$$
$$26 = 25$$

Since $26 = 25$ is false, 9 is not a solution of $3y - 1 = 2y + 7$.

2 Use the addition property of equality.

To **solve an equation** means to find all values of the variable that make the equation true. We can develop an understanding of how to solve equations by referring to the scales shown on the right.

The first scale represents the equation $x - 2 = 3$. The scale is in balance because the weights on the left side and right side are equal. To find x, we must add 2 to the left side. To keep the scale in balance, we must also add 2 to the right side. After doing this, we see that x grams is balanced by 5 grams. Therefore, x must be 5. We say that we have solved the equation $x - 2 = 3$ and that the solution is 5.

In this example, we solved $x - 2 = 3$ by transforming it to a simpler *equivalent equation,* $x = 5$.

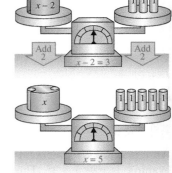

Equivalent Equations

Equations with the same solutions are called **equivalent equations.**

The procedure that we used suggests the following property of equality.

Addition Property of Equality

Adding the same number to both sides of an equation does not change its solution.

For any real numbers a, b, and c,

if $a = b$, then $a + c = b + c$

When we use this property, the resulting equation is *equivalent to the original one.* We will now show how it is used to solve $x - 2 = 3$ algebraically.

EXAMPLE 2   Solve: $x - 2 = 3$

Strategy We will use a property of equality to isolate the variable on one side of the equation.

WHY To solve the original equation, we want to find a simpler equivalent equation of the form $x = \text{a number}$, whose solution is obvious.

Solution
We will use the addition property of equality to isolate x on the left side of the equation. We can undo the subtraction of 2 by adding 2 to both sides.

$$x - 2 = 3 \qquad \text{This is the equation to solve.}$$
$$x - 2 + 2 = 3 + 2 \qquad \text{Add 2 to both sides.}$$
$$x + 0 = 5 \qquad \text{The sum of a number and its opposite is zero: } -2 + 2 = 0.$$
$$x = 5 \qquad \text{When 0 is added to a number, the result is the same number.}$$

Since 5 is obviously the solution of the equivalent equation $x = 5$, the solution of the original equation, $x - 2 = 3$, is also 5. To check this result, we substitute 5 for x in the original equation and simplify.

$$x - 2 = 3$$
$$5 - 2 \overset{?}{=} 3 \qquad \text{Substitute 5 for } x.$$
$$3 = 3 \qquad \text{True}$$

Since the statement is true, 5 is the solution. A more formal way to present this result is to write the solution within braces as a solution set: $\{5\}$.

The Language of Algebra   We solve equations by writing a series of steps that result in an equivalent equation of the form

$$x = \text{a number}$$
$$\text{or}$$
$$\text{a number} = x$$

We say the variable is *isolated* on one side of the equation. *Isolated* means alone or by itself.

EXAMPLE 3   Solve: **a.** $-19 = y - 7$ **b.** $-27 + y = -3$

Strategy We will use a property of equality to isolate the variable on one side of the equation.

WHY To solve the original equation, we want to find a simpler equivalent equation of the form $y = \text{a number}$ or $\text{a number} = y$, whose solution is obvious.

Solution
a. To isolate y on the right side, we use the addition property of equality. We can undo the subtraction of 7 by adding 7 to both sides.

$$-19 = y - 7 \qquad \text{This is the equation to solve.}$$
$$-19 + 7 = y - 7 + 7 \qquad \text{Add 7 to both sides.}$$
$$-12 = y \qquad \text{The sum of a number and its opposite is zero:}$$
$$\qquad\qquad\qquad -7 + 7 = 0.$$

Check: $-19 = y - 7 \qquad \text{This is the original equation.}$
$$-19 \overset{?}{=} -12 - 7 \qquad \text{Substitute } -12 \text{ for } y.$$
$$-19 = -19 \qquad \text{True}$$

Since the statement is true, the solution is -12. The solution set is $\{-12\}$.

Self Check 2
Solve: $n - 16 = 33$
Now Try **Problem 37**

Self Check 3
Solve: **a.** $-5 = b - 38$
b. $-20 + n = 29$
Now Try **Problems 39 and 43**

b. To isolate y, we use the addition property of equality. We can eliminate -27 on the left side by adding its opposite (additive inverse) to both sides.

$$-27 + y = -3 \qquad \text{The equation to solve.}$$

$$-27 + y + 27 = -3 + 27 \qquad \text{Add 27 to both sides.}$$

$$y = 24 \qquad \text{The sum of a number and its opposite is zero:} \\ -27 + 27 = 0.$$

Check:
$$-27 + y = -3 \qquad \text{This is the original equation.}$$
$$-27 + 24 \overset{?}{=} -3 \qquad \text{Substitute 24 for } y.$$
$$-3 = -3 \qquad \text{True}$$

The solution is 24. The solution set is $\{24\}$.

Caution!   After checking a result, be careful when stating your conclusion. Here, it would be incorrect to say:

The solution is -3.

The number we were checking was 24, not -3.

---

3 **Use the subtraction property of equality.**

Since any subtraction can be written as an addition by adding the opposite of the number to be subtracted, the following property is an extension of the addition property of equality.

Subtraction Property of Equality

Subtracting the same number from both sides of an equation does not change its solution.

For any real numbers a, b, and c,

if $a = b$, then $a - c = b - c$

When we use this property, the resulting equation is equivalent to the original one.

Self Check 4

Solve: **a.** $x + \frac{4}{15} = \frac{11}{5}$

b. $0.7 + a = 0.2$

Now Try **Problems 49 and 51**

EXAMPLE 4

Solve: **a.** $x + \dfrac{1}{8} = \dfrac{7}{4}$ **b.** $54.9 + x = 45.2$

Strategy We will use a property of equality to isolate the variable on one side of the equation.

WHY To solve the original equation, we want to find a simpler equivalent equation of the form $x = $ **a number**, whose solution is obvious.

Solution

a. To isolate x, we use the subtraction property of equality. We can undo the addition of $\frac{1}{8}$ by subtracting $\frac{1}{8}$ from both sides.

$$x + \frac{1}{8} = \frac{7}{4} \qquad \text{This is the equation to solve.}$$

$$x + \frac{1}{8} - \frac{1}{8} = \frac{7}{4} - \frac{1}{8} \qquad \text{Subtract } \tfrac{1}{8} \text{ from both sides.}$$

$$x = \frac{7}{4} - \frac{1}{8} \qquad \text{On the left side, } \tfrac{1}{8} - \tfrac{1}{8} = 0.$$

$$x = \frac{7}{4} \cdot \frac{2}{2} - \frac{1}{8} \qquad \text{Build } \tfrac{7}{4} \text{ so that it has a denominator of 8.}$$

$$x = \frac{14}{8} - \frac{1}{8}$$ Multiply the numerators and multiply the denominators.

$$x = \frac{13}{8}$$ Subtract the numerators. Write the result over the common denominator 8.

Verify that $\frac{13}{8}$ is the solution by substituting it for x in the original equation and simplifying.

b. To isolate x, we use the subtraction property of equality. We can undo the addition of 54.9 by subtracting 54.9 from both sides.

$$54.9 + x = 45.2$$ This is the equation to solve.

$$54.9 + x - \mathbf{54.9} = 45.2 - \mathbf{54.9}$$ Subtract 54.9 from both sides.

$$x = -9.7$$ On the left side, $54.9 - 54.9 = 0$.

Check: $$54.9 + x = 45.2$$ This is the original equation.

$$54.9 + (\mathbf{-9.7}) \stackrel{?}{=} 45.2$$ Substitute -9.7 for x.

$$45.2 = 45.2$$ True

The solution is -9.7. The solution set is $\{-9.7\}$.

4   Use the multiplication property of equality.

The first scale shown on the right represents the equation $\frac{x}{3} = 25$. The scale is in balance because the weights on the left side and right side are equal. To find x, we must triple (multiply by 3) the weight on the left side. To keep the scale in balance, we must also triple the weight on the right side. After doing this, we see that x is balanced by 75. Therefore, x must be 75.

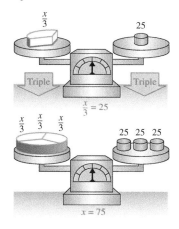

The procedure that we used suggests the following property of equality.

Multiplication Property of Equality

Multiplying both sides of an equation by the same nonzero number does not change its solution.

For any real numbers a, b, and c, where c is not 0,

   if $a = b$, then $ca = cb$

When we use this property, the resulting equation is equivalent to the original one. We will now show how it is used to solve $\frac{x}{3} = 25$ algebraically.

EXAMPLE 5   Solve: $\dfrac{x}{3} = 25$

Strategy We will use a property of equality to isolate the variable on one side of the equation.

WHY To solve the original equation, we want to find a simpler equivalent equation of the form $x =$ **a number**, whose solution is obvious.

Self Check 5

Solve: $\frac{b}{24} = 3$

Now Try Problem 53

Solution

To isolate x, we use the multiplication property of equality. We can undo the division by 3 by multiplying both sides by 3.

$$\frac{x}{3} = 25 \qquad \text{This is the equation to solve.}$$

$$3 \cdot \frac{x}{3} = 3 \cdot 25 \qquad \text{Multiply both sides by 3.}$$

$$\frac{3x}{3} = 75 \qquad \text{Do the multiplications.}$$

$$1x = 75 \qquad \text{Simplify } \tfrac{3x}{3} \text{ by removing the common factor of 3 in the numerator and denominator: } \tfrac{3}{3} = 1.$$

$$x = 75 \qquad \text{The coefficient 1 need not be written since } 1x = x.$$

If we substitute 75 for x in $\frac{x}{3} = 25$, we obtain the true statement $25 = 25$. This verifies that 75 is the solution. The solution set is $\{75\}$.

Since the product of a number and its reciprocal (or multiplicative inverse) is 1, we can solve equations such as $\frac{2}{3}x = 6$, where the coefficient of the variable term is a fraction, as follows.

Self Check 6

Solve: **a.** $\frac{7}{2}x = 21$
b. $-\frac{3}{8}b = 2$

Now Try Problems 61 and 67

EXAMPLE 6

Solve: **a.** $\frac{2}{3}x = 6$ **b.** $-\frac{5}{4}x = 3$

Strategy We will use a property of equality to isolate the variable on one side of the equation.

WHY To solve the original equation, we want to find a simpler equivalent equation of the form $x = $ **a number**, whose solution is obvious.

Solution

a. Since the coefficient of x is $\frac{2}{3}$, we can isolate x by multiplying both sides of the equation by the reciprocal of $\frac{2}{3}$, which is $\frac{3}{2}$.

$$\frac{2}{3}x = 6 \qquad \text{This is the equation to solve.}$$

$$\frac{3}{2} \cdot \frac{2}{3}x = \frac{3}{2} \cdot 6 \qquad \text{To undo the multiplication by } \tfrac{2}{3}, \text{ multiply both sides by the reciprocal of } \tfrac{2}{3}.$$

$$\left(\frac{3}{2} \cdot \frac{2}{3}\right)x = \frac{3}{2} \cdot 6 \qquad \text{Use the associative property of multiplication to group } \tfrac{3}{2} \text{ and } \tfrac{2}{3}.$$

$$1x = 9 \qquad \text{On the left, } \tfrac{3}{2} \cdot \tfrac{2}{3} = 1. \text{ On the right, } \tfrac{3}{2} \cdot 6 = \tfrac{18}{2} = 9.$$

$$x = 9 \qquad \text{The coefficient 1 need not be written since } 1x = x.$$

Check: $\quad \frac{2}{3}x = 6 \qquad \text{This is the original equation.}$

$$\frac{2}{3}(9) \stackrel{?}{=} 6 \qquad \text{Substitute 9 for } x \text{ in the original equation.}$$

$$6 = 6 \qquad \text{On the left side, } \tfrac{2}{3}(9) = \tfrac{18}{3} = 6.$$

Since the statement is true, 9 is the solution. The solution set is $\{9\}$.

The Language of Algebra Variable terms with fractional coefficients can be written in two ways. For example:

$$\frac{2x}{3} = \frac{2}{3}x \qquad \text{and} \qquad -\frac{5a}{4} = -\frac{5}{4}a$$

b. To isolate x, we multiply both sides by the reciprocal of $-\frac{5}{4}$, which is $-\frac{4}{5}$.

$$-\frac{5}{4}x = 3$$ This is the equation to solve.

$$-\frac{4}{5}\left(-\frac{5}{4}x\right) = -\frac{4}{5}(3)$$ To undo the multiplication by $-\frac{5}{4}$, multiply both sides by the reciprocal of $-\frac{5}{4}$.

$$1x = -\frac{12}{5}$$ On the left side, $-\frac{4}{5}\left(-\frac{5}{4}\right) = 1$.
On the right side, $-\frac{4}{5}(3) = -\frac{12}{5}$.

$$x = -\frac{12}{5}$$ The coefficient 1 need not be written since $1x = x$.

The solution is $-\frac{12}{5}$. Verify that this is correct by checking.

5 **Use the division property of equality.**

Since any division can be rewritten as a multiplication by multiplying by the reciprocal, the following property is a natural extension of the multiplication property.

Division Property of Equality

Dividing both sides of an equation by the same nonzero number does not change its solution.

For any real numbers a, b, and c, where c is not 0,

    if $a = b$, then $\dfrac{a}{c} = \dfrac{b}{c}$

When we use this property, the resulting equation is equivalent to the original one.

EXAMPLE 7   Solve: **a.** $2t = 80$ **b.** $-6.02 = -8.6t$

Strategy We will use a property of equality to isolate the variable on one side of the equation.

WHY To solve the original equation, we want to find a simpler equivalent equation of the form $t = \textbf{a number}$ or $\textbf{a number} = t$, whose solution is obvious.

Solution

a. To isolate t on the left side, we use the division property of equality. We can undo the multiplication by 2 by dividing both sides of the equation by 2.

$$2t = 80$$ This is the equation to solve.

$$\frac{2t}{2} = \frac{80}{2}$$ Use the division property of equality: Divide both sides by 2.

$$1t = 40$$ Simplify $\frac{2t}{2}$ by removing the common factor of 2 in the numerator and denominator: $\frac{2}{2} = 1$.

$$t = 40$$ The product of 1 and any number is that number: $1t = t$.

If we substitute 40 for t in $2t = 80$, we obtain the true statement $80 = 80$. This verifies that 40 is the solution. The solution set is $\{40\}$.

Self Check 7
Solve: **a.** $16x = 176$
b. $10.04 = -0.4r$

Now Try **Problems 69 and 79**

The Language of Algebra   Since division by 2 is the same as multiplication by $\frac{1}{2}$, we can also solve $2t = 80$ using the multiplication property of equality. We could also isolate t by multiplying both sides by the *multiplicative inverse* of 2, which is $\frac{1}{2}$:

$$\frac{1}{2} \cdot 2t = \frac{1}{2} \cdot 80$$

b. To isolate t on the right side, we use the division property of equality. We can undo the multiplication by -8.6 by dividing both sides by -8.6.

$$-6.02 = -8.6t \qquad \text{This is the equation to solve.}$$

$$\frac{-6.02}{-8.6} = \frac{-8.6t}{-8.6} \qquad \text{Use the division property of equality: Divide both sides by } -8.6.$$

$$0.7 = t \qquad \text{Do the division: } 8.6\overline{)6.02}. \text{ The quotient of two negative numbers is positive.}$$

The solution is 0.7. Verify that this is correct by checking.

Success Tip   It is usually easier to multiply on each side if the coefficient of the variable term is a *fraction,* and divide on each side if the coefficient is an *integer* or *decimal.*

Self Check 8

Solve: $-h = -12$

Now Try **Problem 81**

EXAMPLE 8   Solve: $-x = 3$

Strategy   The variable x is not isolated, because there is a $-$ sign in front of it. Since the term $-x$ has an understood coefficient of -1, the equation can be written as $-1x = 3$. We need to select a property of equality and use it to isolate the variable on one side of the equation.

WHY   To find the solution of the original equation, we want to find a simpler equivalent equation of the form $x = \textbf{a number}$, whose solution is obvious.

Solution
To isolate x, we can either multiply or divide both sides by -1.

***Multiply both sides by* -1:**

$$-x = 3 \qquad \text{The equation to solve}$$
$$-1x = 3 \qquad \text{Write: } -x = -1x$$
$$(-1)(-1x) = (-1)3$$
$$1x = -3$$
$$x = -3 \qquad 1x = x$$

***Divide both sides by* -1:**

$$-x = 3 \qquad \text{The equation to solve}$$
$$-1x = 3 \qquad \text{Write: } -x = -1x$$
$$\frac{-1x}{-1} = \frac{3}{-1}$$
$$1x = -3 \qquad \text{On the left side, } \tfrac{-1}{-1} = 1.$$
$$x = -3 \qquad 1x = x$$

Check: $-x = 3$ This is the original equation.

$-(-3) \overset{?}{=} 3$ Substitute -3 for x.

$3 = 3$ On the left side, the opposite of -3 is 3.

Since the statement is true, -3 is the solution. The solution set is $\{-3\}$.

ANSWERS TO SELF CHECKS

1. Yes   **2.** 49   **3. a.** 33   **b.** 49   **4. a.** $\frac{29}{15}$ **b.** -0.5 **5.** 72   **6. a.** 6   **b.** $-\frac{16}{3}$ **7. a.** 11   **b.** -25.1 **8.** 12

SECTION **4.3**   STUDY SET

VOCABULARY

Fill in the blanks.

1. An _____, such as $x + 1 = 7$, is a statement indicating that two expressions are equal.

2. Any number that makes an equation true when substituted for the variable is said to _____ the equation. Such numbers are called _____.

3. To _____ an equation means to find all values of the variable that make the equation true.

4. To solve an equation, we _____ the variable on one side of the equal symbol.

5. Equations with the same solutions are called _____ equations.

6. To _____ the solution of an equation, we substitute the value for the variable in the original equation and determine whether the result is a true statement.

CONCEPTS

7. Given $x + 6 = 12$:

  a. What is the left side of the equation?

  b. Is this equation true, false, or neither?

  c. Is 5 the solution?

  d. Does 6 satisfy the equation?

8. For each equation, determine what operation is performed on the variable. Then explain how to undo that operation to isolate the variable.

  a. $x - 8 = 24$

  b. $x + 8 = 24$

  c. $\dfrac{x}{8} = 24$

  d. $8x = 24$

9. Complete the following properties of equality.

  a. If $a = b$, then
  $$a + c = b + \boxed{} \text{ and } a - c = b - \boxed{}$$

  b. If $a = b$, then $ca = \boxed{} b$ and $\dfrac{a}{c} = \dfrac{b}{\boxed{}}$ $(c \neq 0)$

10. a. To solve $\dfrac{h}{10} = 20$, do we multiply both sides of the equation by 10 or 20?

  b. To solve $4k = 16$, do we subtract 4 from both sides of the equation or divide both sides by 4?

11. Simplify each expression.

  a. $x + 7 - 7$ **b.** $y - 2 + 2$

  c. $\dfrac{5t}{5}$ **d.** $6 \cdot \dfrac{h}{6}$

12. a. To solve $-\frac{4}{5}x = 8$, we can multiply both sides by the reciprocal of $-\frac{4}{5}$. What is the reciprocal of $-\frac{4}{5}$?

  b. What is $-\frac{5}{4}\left(-\frac{4}{5}\right)$?

NOTATION

Complete each step to solve the equation.

13. $x - 5 = 45$ ***Check:*** $x - 5 = 45$

  $x - 5 + \boxed{} = 45 + \boxed{}$ $\boxed{} - 5 \boxed{} 45$

  $x = \boxed{}$ $\boxed{} = 45$ True

  $\boxed{}$ is the solution.

14. $8x = 40$ ***Check:*** $8x = 40$

  $\dfrac{8x}{\boxed{}} = \dfrac{40}{\boxed{}}$ $8\left(\boxed{}\right) \overset{?}{=} 40$

  $\boxed{} = 40$ True

  $x = \boxed{}$ $\boxed{}$ is the solution.

15. a. What does the symbol $\overset{?}{=}$ mean?

  b. If you solve an equation and obtain $50 = x$, can you write $x = 50$?

16. Fill in the blank: $-x = \boxed{} x$

GUIDED PRACTICE

Use a check to determine whether the given number is a solution of the equation. **See Example 1.**

17. $6, x + 12 = 28$ **18.** $110, x - 50 = 60$

19. $-8, 2b + 3 = -15$ **20.** $-2, 5t - 4 = -16$

21. $5, 0.5x = 2.9$ **22.** $3.5, 1.2 + x = 4.7$

23. $-6, 33 - \dfrac{x}{2} = 30$ **24.** $-8, \dfrac{x}{4} + 98 = 100$

25. $-2, |c - 8| = 10$ **26.** $-45, |30 - r| = 15$

27. $12, 3x - 2 = 4x - 5$ **28.** $5, 5y + 8 = 3y - 2$

29. $-3, x^2 - x - 6 = 0$ **30.** $-2, y^2 + 5y - 3 = 0$

31. $1, \dfrac{2}{a + 1} + 5 = \dfrac{12}{a + 1}$

32. $4, \dfrac{2t}{t - 2} - \dfrac{4}{t - 2} = 1$

33. $\frac{3}{4}$, $x - \frac{1}{8} = \frac{5}{8}$

34. $\frac{7}{3}$, $-4 = a + \frac{5}{3}$

35. -3, $(x - 4)(x + 3) = 0$

36. 5, $(2x + 1)(x - 5) = 0$

Use a property of equality to solve each equation. Then check the result. See Examples 2–4.

37. $a - 5 = 66$

38. $x - 34 = 19$

39. $9 = p - 9$

40. $3 = j - 88$

41. $x - 1.6 = -2.5$

42. $y - 1.2 = -1.3$

43. $-3 + a = 0$

44. $-1 + m = 0$

45. $d - \frac{1}{9} = \frac{7}{9}$

46. $\frac{7}{15} = b - \frac{1}{15}$

47. $x + 7 = 10$

48. $y + 15 = 24$

49. $s + \frac{1}{5} = \frac{4}{25}$

50. $\frac{1}{6} = h + \frac{4}{3}$

51. $3.5 + f = 1.2$

52. $9.4 + h = 8.1$

Use a property of equality to solve each equation. Then check the result. See Example 5.

53. $\frac{x}{15} = 3$

54. $\frac{y}{7} = 12$

55. $0 = \frac{v}{11}$

56. $\frac{d}{49} = 0$

57. $\frac{d}{-7} = -3$

58. $\frac{c}{-2} = -11$

59. $\frac{y}{0.6} = -4.4$

60. $\frac{y}{0.8} = -2.9$

Use a property of equality to solve each equation. Then check the result. See Example 6.

61. $\frac{4}{5}t = 16$

62. $\frac{11}{15}y = 22$

63. $\frac{2}{3}c = 10$

64. $\frac{9}{7}d = 81$

65. $-\frac{7}{2}r = 21$

66. $-\frac{4}{5}s = 36$

67. $-\frac{5}{4}h = -5$

68. $-\frac{3}{8}t = -3$

Use a property of equality to solve each equation. Then check the result. See Example 7.

69. $4x = 16$

70. $5y = 45$

71. $63 = 9c$

72. $40 = 5t$

73. $23b = 23$

74. $16 = 16h$

75. $-8h = 48$

76. $-9a = 72$

77. $-100 = -5g$

78. $-80 = -5w$

79. $-3.4y = -1.7$

80. $-2.1x = -1.26$

Use a property of equality to solve each equation. Then check the result. See Example 8.

81. $-x = 18$

82. $-y = 50$

83. $-n = \frac{4}{21}$

84. $-w = \frac{11}{16}$

▌TRY IT YOURSELF

Solve each equation. Then check the result.

85. $8.9 = -4.1 + t$

86. $7.7 = -3.2 + s$

87. $-2.5 = -m$

88. $-1.8 = -b$

89. $-\frac{9}{8}x = 3$

90. $-\frac{14}{3}c = 7$

91. $\frac{3}{8} = d + \frac{1}{20}$

92. $\frac{5}{9} = r + \frac{1}{6}$

93. $-15x = -60$

94. $-14x = -84$

95. $-10 = n - 5$

96. $-8 = t - 2$

97. $\frac{h}{-40} = 5$

98. $\frac{x}{-7} = 12$

99. $a - 93 = 2$

100. $18 = x - 3$

101. $0 = \frac{v}{11}$

102. $\frac{d}{49} = 0$

103. $8h = 0$

104. $9a = 0$

105. $23b = 23$

106. $16 = 16h$

LOOK ALIKES . . .

107. **a.** $d + \frac{1}{10} = \frac{3}{4}$ **b.** $d - \frac{1}{10} = \frac{3}{4}$

    c. $\frac{1}{10}d = \frac{3}{4}$ **d.** $10d = \frac{3}{4}$

108. **a.** $x + 4.2 = -18.9$ **b.** $x - 4.2 = -18.9$

    c. $4.2x = -18.9$ **d.** $\frac{x}{4.2} = -18.9$

▌CONCEPT EXTENSIONS

For problems 109 and 110, write the equation that is represented by the first scale and solve that equation. Then draw a representation of the resulting equivalent equation on the second scale.

   ▯ represents x ○ represents 1 unit of weight

109.

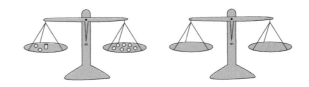

110.

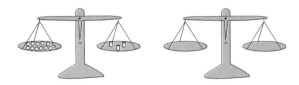

In problems 111 and 112, draw two scales to show how to solve the given equation.

111. $x + 5 = 8$ **112.** $2x = 10$

APPLICATIONS

113. SYNTHESIZERS To find the unknown angle measure, which is represented by x, solve the equation $x + 115 = 180$.

114. STOP SIGNS To find the measure of one angle of the stop sign, which is represented by x, solve the equation $8x = 1,080$.

115. SHARING THE WINNING TICKET When a Florida Lotto Jackpot was won by a group of 16 nurses employed at a Southwest Florida Medical Center, each received $375,000. To find the amount of the jackpot, which is represented by x, solve the equation $\frac{x}{16} = 375,000$.

116. SOCIAL NETWORKS In 2010, the annual revenue generated per employee at Twitter was $142,857. This is $777,143 less than the annual revenue generated per employee at Facebook. To find the annual revenue generated per employee at Facebook, which is represented by x, solve the equation $x - 777,143 = 142,857$. (Source: 37signals.com)

WRITING

117. What does it mean to solve an equation?

118. When solving an equation, we *isolate* the variable on one side of the equation. Write a sentence in which the word *isolate* is used in a different context.

119. Explain the error in the following work.

Solve: $x + 2 = 40$

$x + 2 - 2 = 40$

$x = 40$

120. After solving an equation, how do we check the result?

For each illustration below, describe in words how a scale is used to find the solution to an equation. Then solve the equation algebraically using mathematical symbols.

121.

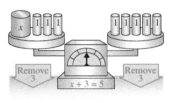

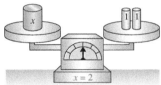

122.

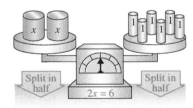

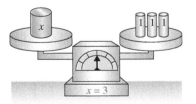

Objectives

1. Use more than one property of equality to solve equations.
2. Simplify expressions to solve equations.
3. Clear equations of fractions and decimals.
4. Identify identities and contradictions.

SECTION **4.4**

More about Solving Equations

ARE YOU READY?

The following problems review some basic skills that are needed when solving equations.

1. Simplify: $4x - 12 - 4x$

2. Simplify: $2a + 2 - 2$

3. Simplify: $5m - 3(4m - 6)$

4. Multiply: $5\left(\dfrac{3}{5}x\right)$

5. Multiply: $18\left(\dfrac{4}{3}n\right)$

6. Multiply: $100 \cdot 0.08$

We have solved simple equations by using properties of equality. We will now expand our equation-solving skills by considering more complicated equations. We want to develop a general strategy that can be used to solve any kind of *linear equation in one variable.*

Linear Equation in One Variable

A **linear equation in one variable** can be written in the form

$$ax + b = c$$

where a, b and c are real numbers and $a \neq 0$.

---

1 **Use more than one property of equality to solve equations.**

Sometimes we must use several properties of equality to solve an equation. For example, on the left side of $2x + 6 = 10$, the variable x is multiplied by 2, and then 6 is added to that product. To isolate x, we use the order of operations rules in reverse. First, we undo the addition of 6, and then we undo the multiplication by 2.

$2x + 6 = 10$	This is the equation to solve.
$2x + 6 - 6 = 10 - 6$	To undo the addition of 6, subtract 6 from both sides.
$2x = 4$	Do the subtractions.
$\dfrac{2x}{2} = \dfrac{4}{2}$	To undo the multiplication by 2, divide both sides by 2.
$x = 2$	Do the divisions.

The solution is 2.

The Language of Algebra   We subtract 6 from both sides to isolate the *variable term,* $2x$. Then we divide both sides by 2 to isolate the *variable,* x.

Self Check 1

Solve: $8x - 13 = 43$

Now Try **Problem 15**

EXAMPLE 1   Solve: $-12x + 5 = 17$

Strategy First we will use a property of equality to isolate the *variable term* on one side of the equation. Then we will use a second property of equality to isolate the *variable* itself.

WHY To solve the original equation, we want to find a simpler equivalent equation of the form $x =$ **a number**, whose solution is obvious.

Solution

- To isolate the variable term, $-12x$, we subtract 5 from both sides to undo the addition of 5.

- To isolate the variable, x, we divide both sides by -12 to undo the multiplication by -12.

$$-12x + 5 = 17 \qquad \text{This is the equation to solve.}$$

$$-12x + 5 - 5 = 17 - 5 \qquad \text{Use the subtraction property of equality: Subtract 5} \\ \text{from both sides to isolate the variable term } -12x.$$

$$-12x = 12 \qquad \text{Do the subtractions: } 5 - 5 = 0 \text{ and } 17 - 5 = 12.$$

$$\frac{-12x}{-12} = \frac{12}{-12} \qquad \text{Use the division property of equality: Divide both sides by} \\ -12 \text{ to isolate } x.$$

$$x = -1 \qquad \text{Do the divisions.}$$

Check: $\quad -12x + 5 = 17 \qquad \text{This is the original equation.}$

$$-12(-1) + 5 \overset{?}{=} 17 \qquad \text{Substitute } -1 \text{ for } x.$$

$$12 + 5 \overset{?}{=} 17 \qquad \text{Do the multiplication on the left side.}$$

$$17 = 17 \qquad \text{True}$$

The solution is -1. The solution set is $\{-1\}$.

> **Caution!** When checking solutions, always use the original equation.

EXAMPLE 2

Solve: $\dfrac{5}{8}m - 2 = -12$

Self Check 2

Solve: $\dfrac{7}{12}a - 6 = -27$

Now Try **Problem 21**

Strategy We will use properties of equality to isolate the variable on one side of the equation.

WHY To solve the original equation, we want to find a simpler equivalent equation of the form $m = \text{a number}$, whose solution is obvious.

Solution

We note that the coefficient of m is $\frac{5}{8}$ and proceed as follows.

- To isolate the variable term $\frac{5}{8}m$, we add 2 to both sides to undo the subtraction of 2.

- To isolate the variable, m, we multiply both sides by $\frac{8}{5}$ to undo the multiplication by $\frac{5}{8}$.

$$\frac{5}{8}m - 2 = -12 \qquad \text{This is the equation to solve.}$$

$$\frac{5}{8}m - 2 + 2 = -12 + 2 \qquad \text{Use the addition property of equality: Add 2 to both} \\ \text{sides to isolate the variable term } \frac{5}{8}m.$$

$$\frac{5}{8}m = -10 \qquad \text{Do the additions: } -2 + 2 = 0 \text{ and } -12 + 2 = -10.$$

$$\frac{8}{5}\left(\frac{5}{8}m\right) = \frac{8}{5}(-10) \qquad \text{Use the multiplication property of equality: Multiply both} \\ \text{sides by } \frac{8}{5} \left(\text{which is the reciprocal of } \frac{5}{8}\right) \text{ to isolate } m.$$

$$m = -16 \qquad \text{On the left side: } \frac{8}{5}\left(\frac{5}{8}\right) = 1 \text{ and } 1m = m. \text{ On the right side:} \\ \frac{8}{5}(-10) = -\frac{8 \cdot 2 \cdot \cancel{5}}{\cancel{5}} = -16.$$

The solution is -16. Verify this by substituting -16 into the original equation. The solution set is $\{-16\}$.

Self Check 3

Solve: $-6.6 - m = -2.7$

Now Try Problem 35

EXAMPLE 3   Solve: $-0.2 = -0.8 - y$

Strategy First, we will use a property of equality to isolate the variable term on one side of the equation. Then we will use a second property of equality to isolate the variable itself.

WHY To solve the original equation, we want to find a simpler equivalent equation of the form **a number** $= y$, whose solution is obvious.

Solution
To isolate the variable term $-y$ on the right side, we eliminate -0.8 by adding 0.8 to both sides.

$$-0.2 = -0.8 - y \qquad \text{This is the equation to solve.}$$
$$-0.2 + \mathbf{0.8} = -0.8 - y + \mathbf{0.8} \qquad \text{Add 0.8 to both sides to isolate } -y.$$
$$0.6 = -y \qquad \text{Do the additions.}$$

Since the term $-y$ has an understood coefficient of -1, the equation can be written as $0.6 = -1y$. To isolate y, we can either multiply both sides or divide both sides by -1. If we choose to divide both sides by -1, we proceed as follows.

$$0.6 = -1y$$
$$\frac{0.6}{-1} = \frac{-1y}{-1} \qquad \text{To undo the multiplication by } -1, \text{ divide both sides by } -1.$$
$$-0.6 = y$$

The solution is -0.6. Verify this by substituting -0.6 into the original equation.   ∎

2 Simplify expressions to solve equations.

When solving equations, we should simplify the expressions that make up the left and right sides before applying any properties of equality. Often, that involves removing parentheses and/or combining like terms.

Self Check 4

Solve: **a.** $4(a + 2) - a = 11$
b. $9x - 5(x - 9) = 1$

Now Try Problems 45 and 47

EXAMPLE 4   Solve: **a.** $3(k + 1) - 5k = 0$ **b.** $8a - 2(a - 7) = 68$

Strategy We will use the distributive property along with the process of combining like terms to simplify the left side of each equation.

WHY It's best to simplify each side of an equation before using a property of equality.

Solution

a. $3(k + 1) - 5k = 0$ $\qquad$ This is the equation to solve.

$$3k + 3 - 5k = 0 \qquad \text{Distribute the multiplication by 3.}$$
$$-2k + 3 = 0 \qquad \text{Combine like terms: } 3k - 5k = -2k.$$
$$-2k + 3 - 3 = 0 - 3 \qquad \text{To undo the addition of 3, subtract 3 from both sides. This isolates the variable term } -2k.$$
$$-2k = -3 \qquad \text{Do the subtractions: } 3 - 3 = 0 \text{ and } 0 - 3 = -3$$
$$\frac{-2k}{-2} = \frac{-3}{-2} \qquad \text{To undo the multiplication by } -2, \text{ divide both sides by } -2. \text{ This isolates the variable } k.$$
$$k = \frac{3}{2} \qquad \text{Simplify: } \frac{-3}{-2} = \frac{3}{2}.$$

Check: $3(k + 1) - 5k = 0$ This is the original equation.

$$3\left(\frac{3}{2} + 1\right) - 5\left(\frac{3}{2}\right) \overset{?}{=} 0$$ Substitute $\frac{3}{2}$ for k.

$$3\left(\frac{5}{2}\right) - 5\left(\frac{3}{2}\right) \overset{?}{=} 0$$ Do the addition within the parentheses. Think of 1 as $\frac{2}{2}$ and then add: $\frac{3}{2} + \frac{2}{2} = \frac{5}{2}$.

$$\frac{15}{2} - \frac{15}{2} \overset{?}{=} 0$$ Do the multiplications.

$$0 = 0$$ True

The solution is $\frac{3}{2}$ and the solution set is $\left\{\frac{3}{2}\right\}$.

Caution!   To check a result, we evaluate each side of the equation following the order of operations rules.

b. $8a - 2(a - 7) = 68$ This is the equation to solve.

$8a - 2a + 14 = 68$ Distribute the multiplication by -2.

$6a + 14 = 68$ Combine like terms: $8a - 2a = 6a$.

$6a + 14 - 14 = 68 - 14$ To undo the addition of 14, subtract 14 from both sides. This isolates the variable term $6a$.

$6a = 54$ Do the subtractions.

$$\frac{6a}{6} = \frac{54}{6}$$ To undo the multiplication by 6, divide both sides by 6. This isolates the variable a.

$a = 9$ Do the divisions.

The solution is 9. Verify this by substituting 9 into the original equation. ∎

When solving an equation, if variables appear on both sides, we can use the addition (or subtraction) property of equality to get all variable terms on one side and all constant terms on the other.

| **EXAMPLE 5**   Solve: $3x - 15 = 4x + 36$ |

Self Check 5

Solve: $30 + 6n = 4n - 2$

Now Try **Problem 57**

Strategy There are variable terms ($3x$ and $4x$) on both sides of the equation. We will eliminate $3x$ from the left side of the equation by subtracting $3x$ from both sides.

WHY To solve for x, all the terms containing x must be on the same side of the equation.

Solution

$3x - 15 = 4x + 36$ This is the equation to solve.

$3x - 15 - 3x = 4x + 36 - 3x$ Subtract 3x from both sides to isolate the variable term on the right side.

$-15 = x + 36$ Combine like terms: $3x - 3x = 0$ and $4x - 3x = x$.

$-15 - 36 = x + 36 - 36$ To undo the addition of 36, subtract 36 from both sides.

$-51 = x$ Do the subtractions.

Check:
$$3x - 15 = 4x + 36 \quad \text{The original equation.}$$
$$3(\mathbf{-51}) - 15 \overset{?}{=} 4(\mathbf{-51}) + 36 \quad \text{Substitute } -51 \text{ for } x.$$
$$-153 - 15 \overset{?}{=} -204 + 36 \quad \text{Do the multiplications.}$$
$$-168 = -168 \quad \text{True}$$

The solution is -51 and the solution set is $\{-51\}$.

3 Clear equations of fractions and decimals.

Equations are usually easier to solve if they don't involve fractions. We can use the multiplication property of equality to clear an equation of fractions by multiplying both sides of the equation by the least common denominator.

Self Check 6

Solve: $\frac{1}{4}x + \frac{1}{2} = -\frac{1}{8}$

***Now Try* Problem 63**

EXAMPLE 6   Solve: $\frac{1}{6}x + \frac{5}{2} = \frac{1}{3}$

Strategy To clear the equations of fractions, we will multiply both sides by their LCD.

WHY It's easier to solve an equation that involves only integers.

Solution

$$\frac{1}{6}x + \frac{5}{2} = \frac{1}{3} \qquad \text{This is the equation to solve.}$$

$$6\left(\frac{1}{6}x + \frac{5}{2}\right) = 6\left(\frac{1}{3}\right) \qquad \begin{array}{l}\text{Multiply both sides by the LCD of } \frac{1}{6}, \frac{5}{2}, \text{ and } \frac{1}{3}, \text{ which is}\\ \text{6. Don't forget the parentheses.}\end{array}$$

$$6\left(\frac{1}{6}x\right) + 6\left(\frac{5}{2}\right) = 6\left(\frac{1}{3}\right) \qquad \text{On the left side, distribute the multiplication by 6.}$$

$$x + 15 = 2 \qquad \begin{array}{l}\text{Do each multiplication: } 6\left(\frac{1}{6}\right) = 1, \ 6\left(\frac{5}{2}\right) = \frac{30}{2} = 15, \text{ and}\\ 6\left(\frac{1}{3}\right) = \frac{6}{3} = 2.\end{array}$$

$$x + 15 - 15 = 2 - 15 \qquad \begin{array}{l}\text{To undo the addition of 15, subtract 15 from both}\\ \text{sides.}\end{array}$$

$$x = -13$$

Check the solution by substituting -13 for x in $\frac{1}{6}x + \frac{5}{2} = \frac{1}{3}$.

> ***Caution!***   Before multiplying both sides of an equation by the LCD, enclose the left and right sides with parentheses or brackets.
>
> $$\left(\frac{1}{6}x + \frac{5}{2}\right) = \left(\frac{1}{3}\right)$$

If an equation contains decimals, it is often convenient to multiply both sides by a power of 10 to change the decimals in the equation to integers.

Self Check 7

Solve:
$(15,000 - x)\,0.08x + 0.07 = 1{,}110$

***Now Try* Problem 71**

EXAMPLE 7   Solve: $0.04(12) + 0.01x = 0.02(12 + x)$

Strategy To clear the equations of decimals, we will multiply both sides by a carefully chosen power of 10.

WHY It's easier to solve an equation that involves only integers.

Solution

The equation contains the decimals 0.04, 0.01, and 0.02. Since the greatest number of decimal places in any one of these numbers is two, we multiply both sides of the equation by 10^2 or 100. This changes 0.04 to 4, and 0.01 to 1, and 0.02 to 2.

$$0.04(12) + 0.01x = 0.02(12 + x)$$

$$100[0.04(12) + 0.01x] = 100[0.02(12 + x)]$$
Multiply both sides by 100. Don't forget the brackets.

$$100 \cdot 0.04(12) + 100 \cdot 0.01x = 100 \cdot 0.02(12 + x)$$
Distribute the multiplication by 100.

$$4(12) + 1x = 2(12 + x)$$
Multiply each decimal by 100 by moving its decimal point 2 places to the right.

$$48 + x = 24 + 2x$$
Distribute the multiplication by 2.

$$48 + x - 24 - x = 24 + 2x - 24 - x$$
Subtract 24 and x from both sides.

$$24 = x$$
Simplify each side.

$$x = 24$$

The solution is 24. Check by substituting 24 for x in the original equation. ∎

The previous examples suggest the following strategy for solving equations. It is important to note that not every step is needed to solve every equation.

Strategy for Solving Linear Equations in One Variable

1. **Clear the equation of fractions or decimals:** Multiply both sides by the LCD to clear fractions or multiply both sides by a power of 10 to clear decimals.
2. **Simplify each side of the equation:** Use the distributive property to remove parentheses, and then combine like terms on each side.
3. **Isolate the variable term on one side:** Add (or subtract) to get the variable term on one side of the equation and a number on the other using the addition (or subtraction) property of equality.
4. **Isolate the variable:** Multiply (or divide) to isolate the variable using the multiplication (or division) property of equality.
5. **Check the result:** Substitute the possible solution for the variable in the *original* equation to see if a true statement results.

EXAMPLE 8 Solve: $\dfrac{7m + 5}{5} = -4m + 1$

Self Check 8
Solve: $6c + 2 = \dfrac{18 - c}{9}$
Now Try **Problem 79**

Strategy We will follow the steps of the equation-solving strategy to solve the equation.

WHY This is the most efficient way to solve a linear equation in one variable.

Solution

$$\frac{7m + 5}{5} = -4m + 1$$
This is the equation to solve.

Step 1 $5\left(\dfrac{7m + 5}{5}\right) = 5(-4m + 1)$
Clear the equation of the fraction by multiplying both sides by 5.

Step 2	$7m + 5 = -20m + 5$	On the left side, remove the common factor 5 in the numerator and denominator. On the right side, distribute the multiplication by 5.

Step 3 $7m + 5 + 20m = -20m + 5 + 20m$ To eliminate the term $-20m$ on the right side, add $20m$ to both sides.

$$27m + 5 = 5$$

Combine like terms:
$7m + 20m = 27m$ and
$-20m + 20m = 0$.

$$27m + 5 - 5 = 5 - 5$$

To isolate the term $27m$, undo the addition of 5 by subtracting 5 from both sides.

$$27m = 0$$ Do the subtractions.

Step 4 $\dfrac{27m}{27} = \dfrac{0}{27}$ To isolate m, undo the multiplication by 27 by dividing both sides by 27.

$$m = 0$$ 0 divided by any nonzero number is 0.

Step 5   Substitute 0 for m in $\frac{7m + 5}{5} = -4m + 1$ to check that the solution is 0.   ■

> *Caution!* Remember that when you multiply one side of an equation by a nonzero number, you must multiply the other side of the equation by the same number.

4 Identify identities and contradictions.

Equations in which some numbers satisfy the equation and others do not are called **conditional equations**. Each of the equations in Examples 1 through 8 are conditional equations because each has only one solutions. However, some equations have no solutions while others have infinitely many solutions.

A linear equation in one variable that is true for all values of the variable is an **identity**. One example is the equation

$$x + x = 2x$$ If we substitute -10 for x, we get the true statement $-20 = -20$. If we substitute 7 for x, we get $14 = 14$, and so on.

Since we can replace x with any number and the equation will be true, all real numbers are solutions of $x + x = 2x$. This equation has infinitely many solutions. Its solution set is written as {all real numbers}.

An equation that is not true for any values of its variable is called a **contradiction**. One example is

$$x = x + 1$$ No number is 1 greater than itself.

Since $x = x + 1$ has no solutions, its solution set is the **empty set,** or **null set,** and is written as $\varnothing$.

Self Check 9

Solve:
$3(x + 5) - 4(x + 4) = -x - 1$

Now Try **Problem 87**

EXAMPLE 9   Solve: $3(x + 8) + 5x = 2(12 + 4x)$

Strategy We will follow the steps of the equation-solving strategy to solve the equation.

WHY This is the most efficient way to solve a linear equation in one variable.

Solution

$$3(x + 8) + 5x = 2(12 + 4x)$$ This is the equation to solve.

$$3x + 24 + 5x = 24 + 8x$$ Distribute the multiplication by 3 and by 2.

$$8x + 24 = 24 + 8x$$ Combine like terms: 3x + 5x = 8x. Note that the sides of the equation are identical.

$$8x - 8x + 24 = 24 + 8x - 8x$$ To eliminate the term 8x on the right side, subtract 8x from both sides.

$$24 = 24$$ Combine like terms on both sides: 8x − 8x = 0.

In this case, the terms involving x drop out and the result is true. This means that any number substituted for x in the original equation will give a true statement. Therefore, *all real numbers* are solutions and this equation is an identity.

> **Success Tip**   Note that at the step $8x + 24 = 24 + 8x$ we know that the equation is an identity.

EXAMPLE 10   Solve: $3(d + 7) - d = 2(d + 10)$

Strategy We will follow the steps of the equation-solving strategy to solve the equation.

WHY This is the most efficient way to solve a linear equation in one variable.

Solution

$$3(d + 7) - d = 2(d + 10)$$ This is the equation to solve.

$$3d + 21 - d = 2d + 20$$ Distribute the multiplication by 3 and by 2.

$$2d + 21 = 2d + 20$$ Combine like terms: 3d − d = 2d.

$$2d + 21 - 2d = 2d + 20 - 2d$$ To eliminate the term 2d on the right side, subtract 2d from both sides.

$$21 = 20$$ Combine like terms on both sides: 2d − 2d = 0.

In this case, the terms involving d drop out and the result is false. This means that any number that is substituted for d in the original equation will give a false statement. Since this equation has *no solution,* it is a contradiction.

> **The Language of Algebra**   *Contradiction* is a form of the word *contradict,* meaning conflicting ideas. During a trial, evidence might be introduced that *contradicts* the testimony of a witness.

Self Check 10

Solve:
$$-4(c - 3) + 2c = 2(10 - c)$$

Now Try **Problem 89**

ANSWERS TO SELF CHECKS

1. 7   **2.** −36   **3.** −3.9   **4. a.** 1   **b.** −11   **5.** −16   **6.** $-\frac{5}{2}$ **7.** 6,000   **8.** 0   **9.** All real numbers; the equation is an identity   **10.** No solution; the equation is a contradiction

SECTION 4.4   STUDY SET

VOCABULARY

Fill in the blanks.

1. $3x + 8 = 10$ is an example of a linear _____ in one variable.

2. To solve $\frac{s}{3} + \frac{1}{4} = -\frac{1}{2}$, we can _____ the equation of the fractions by multiplying both sides by 12.

3. Equations in which some numbers satisfy the equation and others do not are called _____ equations.

4. A linear equation in one variable that is true for all values of the variable is an _____.
   An equation that is not true for any values of its variable is called a _____.

CONCEPTS

Fill in the blanks.

5. To solve $3x - 5 = 1$, we first undo the _____ of 5 by adding 5 to both sides. Then we undo the _____ by 3 by dividing both sides by 3.

6. To solve $\frac{x}{2} + 3 = 5$, we can undo the _____ of 3 by subtracting 3 from both sides. Then we can undo the _____ by 2 by multiplying both sides by 2.

7. a. Combine like terms on the left side of $6x - 8 - 8x = -24$.

   b. Distribute and then combine like terms on the right side of $-20 = 4(3x - 4) - 9x$.

8. Is -2 a solution of the equation?

   a. $6x + 5 = 7$ **b.** $8(x + 3) = 8$

9. Multiply.

   a. $20\left(\frac{3}{5}x\right)$ **b.** $100 \cdot 0.02x$

10. By what must you multiply both sides of $\frac{2}{3} - \frac{1}{2}b = -\frac{4}{3}$ to clear it of fractions?

11. By what must you multiply both sides of $0.7x + 0.3(x - 1) = 0.5x$ to clear it of decimals?

12. a. Simplify: $3x + 5 - x$

   b. Solve: $3x + 5 = 9$

   c. Evaluate $3x + 5 - x$ for $x = 9$.

   d. Check: Is -1 a solution of $3x + 5 - x = 9$?

NOTATION

Complete each step.

13. Solve:
$$2x - 7 = 21$$
$$2x - 7 \boxed{} = 21 \boxed{}$$
$$2x = 28$$
$$\frac{2x}{\boxed{}} = \frac{28}{\boxed{}}$$
$$x = 14$$

   Check:
$$2x - 7 = 21$$
$$2\left(\boxed{}\right) - 7 \boxed{} 21$$
$$\boxed{} - 7 \overset{?}{=} 21$$
$$\boxed{} = 21$$

   $\boxed{}$ is the solution.

14. A student multiplied both sides of $\frac{3}{4}t + \frac{5}{8} = \frac{1}{2}t$ by 8 to clear it of fractions, as shown below. Explain his error in showing this step.
$$8 \cdot \tfrac{3}{4}t + \tfrac{5}{8} = 8 \cdot \tfrac{1}{2}t$$

GUIDED PRACTICE

Solve each equation and check the result. See Examples 1–2.

15. $2x + 5 = 17$ **16.** $3x - 5 = 13$

17. $5q - 2 = 23$ **18.** $4p + 3 = 43$

19. $-33 = 5t + 2$ **20.** $-55 = 3w + 5$

21. $\frac{5}{6}k - 5 = 10$ **22.** $\frac{2}{5}c - 12 = 2$

23. $-\frac{7}{16}h + 28 = 21$ **24.** $-\frac{5}{8}h + 25 = 15$

25. $\frac{t}{3} + 2 = 6$ **26.** $\frac{x}{5} - 5 = -12$

27. $-3p + 7 = -3$ **28.** $-2r + 8 = -1$

29. $-5 - 2d = 0$ **30.** $-8 - 3c = 0$

31. $2(-3) + 4y = 14$ **32.** $4(-1) + 3y = 8$

33. $0.7 - 4y = 1.7$ **34.** $0.3 - 2x = -0.9$

Solve each equation and check the result. See Example 3.

35. $1.2 - x = -1.7$ **36.** $0.6 = 4.1 - x$

37. $-6 - y = -2$ **38.** $-1 - h = -9$

Solve each equation and check the result. See Example 4.

39. $3(2y - 2) - y = 5$ **40.** $2(-3a + 2) + a = 2$

41. $4(5b) + 2(6b - 1) = -34$

42. $9(x + 11) + 5(13 - x) = 0$

43. $-(4 - m) = -10$ **44.** $-(6 - t) = -12$

45. $10.08 = 4(0.5x + 2.5)$ **46.** $-3.28 = 8(1.5y - 0.5)$

47. $6a - 3(3a - 4) = 30$ **48.** $16y - 8(3y - 2) = -24$

49. $-(19 - 3s) - (8s + 1) = 35$

50. $2(3x) - 5(3x + 1) = 58$

Solve each equation and check the result. See Example 5.

51. $5x = 4x + 7$ **52.** $3x = 2x + 2$

53. $8y + 44 = 4y$ **54.** $9y + 36 = 6y$

55. $60r - 50 = 15r - 5$ **56.** $100f - 75 = 50f + 75$

57. $8y - 2 = 4y + 16$ **58.** $7 + 3w = 4 + 9w$

59. $2 - 3(x - 5) = 4(x - 1)$

60. $2 - (4x + 7) = 3 + 2(x + 2)$

61. $3(A + 2) = 2(A - 7)$

62. $9(T - 1) = 6(T + 2) - T$

Solve each equation and check the result. See Example 6.

63. $\frac{1}{8}y - \frac{1}{2} = \frac{1}{4}$ **64.** $\frac{1}{15}x - \frac{4}{5} = \frac{2}{3}$

65. $\frac{1}{3} = \frac{5}{6}x + \frac{2}{9}$ **66.** $\frac{2}{3} = -\frac{2}{3}x + \frac{3}{4}$

67. $\frac{1}{6}y + \frac{1}{4}y = -1$ **68.** $\frac{1}{3}x + \frac{1}{4}x = -2$

69. $\frac{2}{3}y + 2 = \frac{1}{5} + y$ **70.** $\frac{2}{5}x + 1 = \frac{1}{3} + x$

Solve each equation and check the result. See Example 7.

71. $0.06(s + 9) - 1.24 = -0.08s$

72. $0.08(x + 50) - 0.16x = 0.04(50)$

73. $0.09(t + 50) + 0.15t = 52.5$

74. $0.08(x - 100) = 44.5 - 0.07x$

75. $0.06(a + 200) + 0.1a = 172$

76. $0.03x + 0.05(6,000 - x) = 280$

77. $0.4b - 0.1(b - 100) = 70$

78. $0.105x + 0.06(20,000 - x) = 1,740$

Solve each equation and check the result. See Example 8.

79. $\frac{10 - 5s}{3} = s$ **80.** $\frac{40 - 8s}{5} = -2s$

81. $\frac{7t - 9}{16} = t$ **82.** $\frac{11r + 68}{3} = -3$

83. $\frac{5(1 - x)}{6} = -x + 1$ **84.** $\frac{3(14 - u)}{8} = -3u + 6$

85. $\frac{3(d - 8)}{4} = \frac{2(d + 1)}{3}$ **86.** $\frac{3(c - 2)}{2} = \frac{2(2c + 3)}{5}$

Solve each equation, if possible. See Examples 9–10.

87. $8x + 3(2 - x) = 5x + 6$

88. $5(x + 2) = 5x - 2$

89. $-3(s + 2) = -2(s + 4) - s$

90. $21(b - 1) + 3 = 3(7b - 6)$

91. $2(3z + 4) = 2(3z - 2) + 13$

92. $x + 7 = \frac{2x + 6}{2} + 4$

93. $4(y - 3) - y = 3(y - 4)$

94. $5(x + 3) - 3x = 2(x + 8)$

TRY IT YOURSELF

Solve each equation, if possible. Check the result.

95. $3x - 8 - 4x - 7x = -2 - 8$

96. $-6t - 7t - 5t - 1 = 12 - 3$

97. $0.05a + 0.01(90) = 0.02(a + 90)$

98. $0.03x + 0.05(2,000 - x) = 99.5$

99. $\frac{3(b + 2)}{2} = \frac{4b - 10}{4}$

100. $\frac{2(5a - 7)}{4} = \frac{9(a - 1)}{3}$

101. $4(a - 3) = -2(a - 6) + 6a$

102. $9(t + 2) = -6(t - 3) + 15t$

103. $10 - 2y = 8$ **104.** $7 - 7x = -21$

105. $2n - \frac{3}{4}n = \frac{1}{2}n + \frac{13}{3}$ **106.** $\frac{5}{6}n + 3n = -\frac{1}{3}n - \frac{11}{9}$

107. $-\frac{2}{3}z + 4 = 8$ **108.** $-\frac{7}{5}x + 9 = -5$

109. $-2(9 - 3s) - (5s + 2) = -25$

110. $4(x - 5) - 3(12 - x) = 7$

111. $4x = 3x$ **112.** $-8n = 6n$

113. $-(2t - 0.71) = 0.9(1.4 - t)$

114. $-(9m - 11.13) = 7.7(6 + m)$

LOOK ALIKES . . .

Simplify each expression and solve each equation.

115. a. $-2(9 - 3x) - (5x + 2)$
      b. $-2(9 - 3x) - (5x + 2) = -25$

116. a. $4(x - 5) - 3(12 - x)$
      b. $4(x - 5) - 3(12 - x) = 7$

117. a. $0.6 - 0.2(x + 1)$
      b. $0.6 - 0.2(x + 1) = 0.4$

118. a. $2(6n + 4) + 4(3n + 2) + 2$
      b. $2(6n + 5) = 4(3n + 2) + 2$

CONCEPT EXTENSIONS

⬚ represents x ○ represents 1 unit of weight

119. a. What equation is represented by the first scale shown below?

   b. The equation can be solved in two steps. Complete the remaining drawings to illustrate each step of the solution process.

Step 1:

Step 2:

120. a. What equation is represented by the first scale shown below?

    b. The equation can be solved in three steps. Complete the remaining drawings to illustrate each step of the solution process.

Step 1:

Step 2:

Step 3:

121. Consider the equation: $2x + 4 = $
Insert a number in the blank so that . . .

    a. the solution of the equation is a positive number

    b. the solution of the equation is a negative number

    c. the solution of the equation is 0

122. Consider the equation: $3x - 8 = $
Insert a number or algebraic expression in the blank so that

    a. it is a conditional equation

    b. it is an identity

    c. it is a contradiction

▌ WRITING

123. To solve $3x - 4 = 5x + 1$, one student began by subtracting $3x$ from both sides. Another student solved the same equation by first subtracting $5x$ from both sides. Will the students get the same solution? Explain why or why not.

124. What does it mean to clear an equation such as $\frac{1}{4} + \frac{1}{2}x = \frac{3}{8}$ of the fractions?

125. Explain the error in the following solution.

$$
\begin{aligned}
\text{Solve:} \qquad 2x + 4 &= 30 \\
\frac{2x}{2} + 4 &= \frac{30}{2} \\
x + 4 &= 15 \\
x + 4 - 4 &= 15 - 4 \\
x &= 11
\end{aligned}
$$

126. Write an equation that is an identity. Explain why every real number is a solution.

Objectives

1 Use formulas from business.

2 Use formulas from science.

3 Use formulas from geometry.

4 Solve for a specified variable.

SECTION **4.5**
Formulas

ARE YOU READY?

The following problems review some basic skills that are needed when working with formulas.

1. How many variables does each equation contain?

    a. $4x + 3 = 15$

    b. $P = 2l + 2w$

2. Simplify: $a + d - a$

3. Multiply: $4 \cdot \frac{1}{4}x$

4. Multiply: $c(8 - x)$

5. If $2 = t$, is it also true that $t = 2$?

6. Simplify: $\dfrac{b}{b}$

A **formula** is an equation that states a mathematical relationship between two or more variables. Formulas are used in fields such as business, science, and geometry.

1   Use formulas from business.

A formula for retail price: To make a profit, a merchant must sell an item for more than he or she paid for it. The price at which the merchant sells the product, called the **retail price,** is the *sum* of what the item cost the merchant plus the **markup.** Using r to represent the retail price, c the cost, and m the markup, we can write this formula as

$$r = c + m \qquad \text{Retail price} = \text{cost} + \text{markup}$$

A formula for profit: The **profit** a business makes is the *difference* between the **revenue** (the money it takes in) and the cost. Using p to represent the profit, r the revenue, and c the cost, we can write this formula as

$$p = r - c \qquad \text{Profit} = \text{revenue} - \text{cost}$$

If we are given the values of all but one of the variables in a formula, we can use our equation-solving skills to find the value of the remaining variable.

EXAMPLE 1   *Films*   Estimates are that Warner Brothers made a $219 million profit on the film *Harry Potter and the Half-Blood Prince*. If the studio received $469 million in worldwide box office revenue, find the cost to make and distribute the film. (Source: www.thenumbers.com, June 2010)

Copyright © Warner Bros./courtesy Everett Collection/Everett Collection

Strategy   To find the cost to make and distribute the film, we will substitute the given values in the formula $p = r - c$ and solve for c.

WHY   The variable c in the formula represents the unknown cost.

Solution

The film made $219 million (the profit p) and the studio took in $469 million (the revenue r). To find the cost c, we proceed as follows.

$$p = r - c \qquad \text{This is the formula for profit.}$$

$$219 = 469 - c \qquad \text{Substitute 219 for } p \text{ and 469 for } r.$$

$$219 - 469 = 469 - c - 469 \qquad \begin{array}{l}\text{To eliminate 469 on the right side,} \\ \text{subtract 469 from both sides.}\end{array}$$

$$-250 = -c \qquad \text{Do the subtractions.}$$

$$\frac{-250}{-1} = \frac{-c}{-1} \qquad \text{To solve for } c, \text{ divide (or multiply) both sides by } -1.$$

$$250 = c \qquad \text{The units are millions of dollars.}$$

It cost $250 million to make and distribute the film.

Self Check 1

A PTA spaghetti dinner made a profit of $275.50. If the cost to host the dinner was $1,235, how much revenue did it generate?

Now Try **Problem 11**

A formula for simple interest: When money is borrowed, the lender expects to be paid back the amount of the loan plus an additional charge for the use of the money, called **interest.** When money is deposited in a bank, the depositor is paid for the use of the money. The money the deposit earns is also called interest.

Interest is computed in two ways: either as **simple interest** or as **compound interest.** Simple interest is the *product* of the principal (the amount of money that is invested, deposited, or borrowed), the annual interest rate, and the length of time in years. Using I to represent the simple interest, P the principal, r the annual interest rate, and t the time in years, we can write this formula as

$$I = Prt \quad \text{Interest = principal} \cdot \text{rate} \cdot \text{time}$$

> **The Language of Algebra** The word *annual* means occurring once a year. An *annual* interest rate is the interest rate paid per year.

Self Check 2
A father loaned his daughter $12,200 at a 2% annual simple interest rate for a down payment on a house. If the interest on the loan amounted to $610, for how long was the loan?

Now Try **Problem 15**

EXAMPLE 2 *Retirement Income* One year after investing $15,000, a retired couple received a check for $1,125 in interest. Find the interest rate their money earned that year.

Strategy To find the interest rate, we will substitute the given values in the formula $I = Prt$ and solve for r.

WHY The variable r represents the unknown interest rate.

Solution
The couple invested $15,000 (the principal P) for 1 year (the time t) and made $1,125 (the interest I). To find the annual interest rate r, we proceed as follows.

$I = Prt$	This is the formula for simple interest.
$1,125 = 15,000r(1)$	Substitute 1,125 for I, 15,000 for P, and 1 for t.
$1,125 = 15,000r$	Simplify the right side.
$\dfrac{1,125}{15,000} = \dfrac{15,000r}{15,000}$	To solve for r, undo the multiplication by 15,000 by dividing both sides by 15,000.
$0.075 = r$	Do the divisions.
$7.5\% = r$	To write 0.075 as a percent, multiply 0.075 by 100 by moving the decimal point two places to the right and inserting a % symbol.

The couple received an annual rate of 7.5% that year on their investment. We can display the facts of the problem in a table.

	P	$\cdot$	r	$\cdot$	$t =$	I
Investment	15,000		0.075		1	1,125

> ***Caution!*** When using the formula $I = Prt$, always write the interest rate r (which is given as a percent) as a decimal (or fraction) before performing any calculations.

2 Use formulas from science.

A formula for distance traveled: If we know the average rate (of speed) at which we will be traveling and the time we will be traveling at that rate, we can find the distance traveled. Using d to represent the distance, r the average rate, and t the time, we can write this formula as

$d = rt$ Distance = rate · time

EXAMPLE 3 *Whales* As they migrate from the Bering Sea to Baja California, gray whales swim for about 20 hours each day, covering a distance of approximately 70 miles. Estimate their average swimming rate in miles per hour (mph).

Strategy To find the swimming rate, we will substitute the given values in the formula $d = rt$ and solve for r.

WHY The variable r represents the unknown average swimming rate.

Solution
The whales swam 70 miles (the distance d) in 20 hours (the time t). To find their average swimming rate r, we proceed as follows.

$d = rt$ This is the formula for distance traveled.

$70 = r(20)$ Substitute 70 for d and 20 for t.

$\dfrac{70}{20} = \dfrac{20r}{20}$ To solve for r, undo the multiplication by 20 by dividing both sides by 20.

$3.5 = r$ Do the divisions.

The whales' average swimming rate is 3.5 mph. The facts of the problem can be shown in a table.

	r · t = d		
Gray whale	3.5	20	70

A formula for converting temperatures: In the American system, temperature is measured on the Fahrenheit scale. The Celsius scale is used to measure temperature in the metric system. The formula that relates a Fahrenheit temperature F to a Celsius temperature C is:

$$C = \frac{5}{9}(F - 32)$$

EXAMPLE 4 Convert the temperature shown on the City Savings sign to degrees Fahrenheit.

Strategy To find the temperature in degrees Fahrenheit, we will substitute the given Celsius temperature in the formula $C = \frac{5}{9}(F - 32)$ and solve for F.

CITY SAVINGS
TEMP 30°C

Self Check 3
An elevator travels at an average rate of 288 feet per minute. How long will it take the elevator to climb 30 stories, a distance of 360 feet?
Now Try **Problem 19**

Self Check 4
Change $-175°C$, the temperature on Saturn, to degrees Fahrenheit.
Now Try **Problem 25**

WHY The variable F represents the unknown temperature in degrees Fahrenheit.

Solution

The temperature in degrees Celsius is 30°. To find the temperature in degrees Fahrenheit F, we proceed as follows.

$$C = \frac{5}{9}(F - 32)$$ This is the formula for temperature conversion.

$$30 = \frac{5}{9}(F - 32)$$ Substitute 30 for C, the Celsius temperature.

$$\frac{9}{5} \cdot 30 = \frac{9}{5} \cdot \frac{5}{9}(F - 32)$$ To undo the multiplication by $\frac{5}{9}$, multiply both sides by the reciprocal of $\frac{5}{9}$.

$$54 = F - 32$$ Do the multiplications.

$$54 + 32 = F - 32 + 32$$ To isolate F, undo the subtraction of 32 by adding 32 to both sides.

$$86 = F$$

30°C is equivalent to 86°F.

3 Use formulas from geometry.

To find the **perimeter** of a plane (two-dimensional, flat) geometric figure, such as a rectangle or triangle, we find the distance around the figure by computing the sum of the lengths of its sides. Perimeter is measured in American units, such as inches, feet, yards, and in metric units such as millimeters, meters, and kilometers.

Perimeter Formulas

$P = 2l + 2w$ (rectangle)

$P = 4s$ (square)

$P = a + b + c$ (triangle)

The Language of Algebra When you hear the word *perimeter,* think of the distance around the "rim" of a flat figure.

Self Check 5

The largest flag that consistently flies is the flag of Brazil in Brasilia, the country's capital. It has a perimeter of 1,116 feet and a length of 328 feet. Find its width.

Now Try **Problem 27**

EXAMPLE 5 *Flags* The largest flag ever flown was an American flag that had a perimeter of 1,520 feet and a length of 505 feet. It was hoisted on cables across Hoover Dam to celebrate the 1996 Olympic Torch Relay. Find the width of the flag.

w

505 ft

Strategy To find the width of the flag, we will substitute the given values in the formula $P = 2l + 2w$ and solve for w.

WHY The variable w represents the unknown width of the flag.

Solution

The perimeter P of the rectangular-shaped flag is 1,520 ft and the length l is 505 ft. To find the width w, we proceed as follows.

$$P = 2l + 2w$$ This is the formula for the perimeter of a rectangle.

$$1{,}520 = 2(505) + 2w$$ Substitute 1,520 for P and 505 for l.

$$1{,}520 = 1{,}010 + 2w$$ Do the multiplication.

$$510 = 2w$$ To undo the addition of 1,010, subtract 1,010 from both sides.

$$255 = w$$ To isolate w, undo the multiplication by 2 by dividing both sides by 2.

The width of the flag is 255 feet. If its length is 505 feet and its width is 255 feet, its perimeter is $2(505) + 2(255) = 1{,}010 + 510 = 1{,}520$ feet, as given. ■

The **area** of a plane (two-dimensional, flat) geometric figure is the amount of surface that it encloses. Area is measured in square units, such as square inches, square feet, square yards, and square meters (written as in.^{2}, ft^2, yd^2, and m^2, respectively).

Area Formulas

$A = lw$ (rectangle)

$A = s^2$ (square)

$A = \dfrac{1}{2}bh$ (triangle)

$A = \dfrac{1}{2}h(B + b)$ (trapezoid)

Circle Formulas

$D = 2r$ (diameter)

$r = \dfrac{1}{2}D$ (radius)

$C = 2\pi r = \pi D$ (circumference)

$A = \pi r^2$ (area)

EXAMPLE 6   **a.** What is the circumference of a circle with diameter 14 feet? Round to the nearest tenth of a foot.   **b.** What is the area of the circle? Round to the nearest tenth of a square foot.

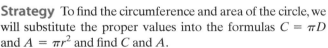
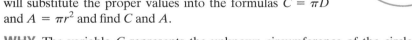
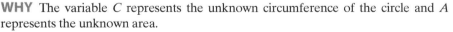

Diameter = 14 ft

Radius

Strategy To find the circumference and area of the circle, we will substitute the proper values into the formulas $C = \pi D$ and $A = \pi r^2$ and find C and A.

WHY The variable C represents the unknown circumference of the circle and A represents the unknown area.

Solution

a. Recall that the circumference of a circle is the distance around it. To find the circumference C of a circle with diameter D equal to 14 ft, we proceed as follows.

$$C = \pi D$$ This is the formula for the circumference of a circle. πD means $\pi \cdot D$.

$$C = \pi(14)$$ Substitute 14 for D, the diameter of the circle.

$$= 14\pi$$ The exact circumference of the circle is 14π.

Self Check 6

Find the circumference of a circle with a radius of 10 inches. Round to the nearest hundredth of an inch.

Now Try **Problem 28**

$$\approx 43.98229715$$

To use a scientific calculator to approximate the circumference, enter $\boxed{\pi}$ $\boxed{\times}$ 14 $\boxed{=}$. If you do not have a calculator, use 3.14 as an approximation of π. (Answers may vary slightly depending on which approximation of π is used.)

The circumference is exactly 14π ft. Rounded to the nearest tenth, this is 44.0 ft.

b. The radius r of the circle is one-half the diameter, or 7 feet. To find the area A of the circle, we proceed as follows.

$$A = \pi r^2$$ This is the formula for the area of a circle. πr^2 means $\pi \cdot r^2$.

$$A = \pi (7)^2$$ Substitute 7 for r, the radius of the circle.

$$= 49\pi$$ Evaluate the exponential expression: $7^2 = 49$. The exact area is 49π ft^2.

$$\approx 153.93804$$ To use a calculator to approximate the area, enter 49 $\boxed{\times}$ $\boxed{\pi}$ $\boxed{=}$.

The area is exactly 49π ft^2. To the nearest tenth, the area is 153.9 ft^2.

> **Caution!** When an approximation of π is used in a calculation, it produces an approximate answer. Remember to use an *is approximately equal to* symbol $\approx$ in your solution to show that.

The **volume** of a three-dimensional geometric solid is the amount of space it encloses. Volume is measured in cubic units, such as cubic inches, cubic feet, and cubic meters (written as in.^{3}, ft^3, and m^3, respectively). Several volume formulas are given at the top of page 63

Self Check 7

Find the volume of a cone whose base has a radius of 12 meters and whose height is 9 meters. Round to the nearest tenth of a cubic meter. Use the formula $V = \frac{1}{3}\pi r^2 h$.

Now Try **Problem 29**

EXAMPLE 7   Find the volume of the cylinder. Round to the nearest tenth of a cubic centimeter.

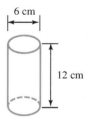

Strategy To find the volume of the cylinder, we will substitute the proper values into the formula $V = \pi r^2 h$ and find V.

WHY The variable V represents the unknown volume.

Solution
Since the radius of a circle is one-half its diameter, the radius r of the circular base of the cylinder is $\frac{1}{2}(6\text{ cm}) = 3$ cm. The height h of the cylinder is 12 cm. To find volume V of the cylinder, we proceed as follows.

$$V = \pi r^2 h$$ This is the formula for the volume of a cylinder. $\pi r^2 h$ means $\pi \cdot r^2 \cdot h$.

$$V = \pi (3)^2 (12)$$ Substitute 3 for r and 12 for h.

$$= \pi (9)(12)$$ Evaluate the exponential expression.

$$= 108\pi$$ Multiply. The exact volume is 108π cm^3.

$$\approx 339.2920066$$ Use a calculator to approximate the volume.

To the nearest tenth, the volume is 339.3 cubic centimeters. This can be written as 339.3 cm^3.

Volume Formulas

$V = lwh$ (rectangular solid) $V = \pi r^2 h$ (cylinder)

$V = s^3$ (cube)

$V = \dfrac{4}{3}\pi r^3$ (sphere) $V = \dfrac{1}{3}\pi r^2 h$ (cone)

$V = \dfrac{1}{3}Bh$* (pyramid)

*Where B is the area of the base.

---

4 **Solve for a specified variable.**

Suppose a shopper wishes to calculate the markup m on several items, knowing their retail price r and their cost c to the merchant. It would take a lot of time to substitute values for r and c into the formula for retail price $r = c + m$ and then repeatedly solve for m. A better way is to solve the formula for m first, substitute values for r and c, and then compute m directly.

To **solve a formula for a specified variable** means to isolate that variable on one side of the equation, with all other variables and constants on the opposite side.

EXAMPLE 8   Solve the formula for retail price, $r = c + m$ for m.

Strategy To solve for m, we will focus on it as if it is the only variable in the equation. We will use a strategy similar to that used to solve linear equations in one variable to isolate m on one side. (See page 51 if you need to review the strategy.)

WHY We can solve the formula as if it were an equation in one variable because all the other variables are treated as if they were numbers (constants).

Solution

To solve for m, we will isolate m on this side of the equation.

$r = c + m$

$r - c = c + m - c$ To isolate m, undo the addition of c by subtracting c from both sides.

$r - c = m$ Simplify the right side: $c - c = 0$.

$m = r - c$ Reverse the sides of the equation so that m is on the left.   ∎

> **The Language of Algebra**   We say that the formula is *solved for m* because m is alone on one side of the equation and the other side does not contain m.

EXAMPLE 9   Solve $A = \frac{1}{2}bh$ for b.

Strategy To solve for b, we will treat b as the only variable in the equation and use properties of equality to isolate it on one side. We will treat the other variables as if they were numbers (constants).

WHY To solve for a specified variable means to isolate it on one side of the equation.

Solution

We use the same steps to solve an equation for a specified variable that we use to solve equations with only one variable.

Self Check 8

Solve the formula for profit, $p = r - c$, for r.

Now Try **Problem 31**

Self Check 9

Solve $A = \frac{1}{2}r^2 a$ for a.

Now Try **Problem 37**

To solve for b, we will isolate b on this side of the equation.

$$A = \frac{1}{2}bh$$

$$2 \cdot A = 2 \cdot \frac{1}{2}bh$$ To clear the equation of the fraction, multiply both sides by 2.

$$2A = bh$$ Simplify.

$$\frac{2A}{h} = \frac{bh}{h}$$ To isolate b, undo the multiplication by h by dividing both sides by h.

$$\frac{2A}{h} = b$$ On the right side, remove the common factor of h: $\frac{bh}{h} = b$.

$$b = \frac{2A}{h}$$ Reverse the sides of the equation so that b is on the left.

Self Check 10

Solve $P = 2l + 2w$ for w.

Now Try Problem 45

EXAMPLE 10 Solve $P = 2l + 2w$ for l.

Strategy To solve for l, we will treat l as the only variable in the equation and use properties of equality to isolate it on one side. We will treat the other variables as if they were numbers (constants).

WHY To solve for a specified variable means to isolate it on one side of the equation.

Solution

To solve for l, we will isolate l on this side of the equation.

$$P = 2l + 2w$$

$$P - 2w = 2l + 2w - 2w$$ To undo the addition of $2w$, subtract $2w$ from both sides.

$$P - 2w = 2l$$ Combine like terms: $2w - 2w = 0$.

$$\frac{P - 2w}{2} = \frac{2l}{2}$$ To isolate l, undo the multiplication by 2 by dividing both sides by 2.

$$\frac{P - 2w}{2} = l$$ Simplify the right side.

We can write the result as $l = \frac{P - 2w}{2}$.

Caution! Do not try to simplify the result this way:

$$l = \frac{P - \overset{1}{2}w}{\underset{1}{2}}$$

This step is incorrect because 2 is not a factor of the entire numerator.

Self Check 11

Solve $x + 3y = 12$ for y.

Now Try Problem 47

EXAMPLE 11 In Module 5 we will work with equations that involve the variables x and y, such as $3x + 2y = 4$. Solve this equation for y.

Strategy To solve for y, we will treat y as the only variable in the equation and use properties of equality to isolate it on one side.

WHY To solve for a specified variable means to isolate it on one side of the equation.

Solution

$$3x + 2y = 4$$

To solve for y, we will isolate y on this side of the equation.

$$3x + 2y - 3x = 4 - 3x$$

To eliminate 3x on the left side, subtract 3x from both sides.

$$2y = 4 - 3x$$

Combine like terms: $3x - 3x = 0$.

$$\frac{2y}{2} = \frac{4 - 3x}{2}$$

To isolate y, undo the multiplication by 2 by dividing both sides by 2.

$$y = \frac{4}{2} - \frac{3x}{2}$$

Write $\frac{4 - 3x}{2}$ as the difference of two fractions with like denominators, $\frac{4}{2}$ and $\frac{3x}{2}$.

$$y = 2 - \frac{3}{2}x$$

Simplify: $\frac{4}{2} = 2$. Write $\frac{3x}{2}$ as $\frac{3}{2}x$.

$$y = -\frac{3}{2}x + 2$$

On the right side, write the x term first.

> **Success Tip** When solving for a specified variable, there is often more than one way to express the result.

EXAMPLE 12 Solve $V = \pi r^2 h$ for r^2.

Strategy To solve for r^2, we will treat it as the only variable expression in the equation and isolate it on one side.

WHY To solve for a specified variable means to isolate it on one side of the equation.

Solution

$$V = \pi r^2 h$$

To solve for r^2, we will isolate r^2 on this side of the equation.

$$\frac{V}{\pi h} = \frac{\pi r^2 h}{\pi h}$$

$\pi r^2 h$ means $\pi \cdot r^2 \cdot h$. To isolate r^2, undo the multiplication by π and h on the right side by dividing both sides by πh.

$$\frac{V}{\pi h} = r^2$$

On the right side, remove the common factors of π and h: $\frac{\overset{1}{\pi} r^2 \overset{1}{h}}{\underset{1}{\pi} \underset{1}{h}} = r^2$.

$$r^2 = \frac{V}{\pi h}$$

Reverse the sides of the equation so that r^2 is on the left.

Self Check 12

Solve $V = lwh$ for w.

Now Try Problem 55

ANSWERS TO SELF CHECKS

1. \$1,510.50 **2.** 2.5 yr **3.** 1.25 min **4.** $-283°F$ **5.** 230 ft **6.** 62.83 in. **7.** 1,357.2 m^3
8. $r = p + c$ **9.** $a = \frac{2A}{r^2}$ **10.** $w = \frac{P - 2l}{2}$ **11.** $y = 4 - \frac{1}{3}x$ or $y = -\frac{1}{3}x + 4$ **12.** $w = \frac{V}{lh}$

SECTION 4.5 STUDY SET

VOCABULARY

Fill in the blanks.

1. A _____ is an equation that is used to state a known relationship between two or more variables.

2. The distance around a plane geometric figure is called its _____, and the amount of surface that it encloses is called its _____.

3. The _____ of a three-dimensional geometric solid is the amount of space it encloses.

4. The formula $a = P - b - c$ is _____ for a because a is isolated on one side of the equation and the other side does not contain a.

CONCEPTS

5. Use variables to write the formula relating:

   a. Time, distance, rate

   b. Markup, retail price, cost

   c. Costs, revenue, profit

   d. Interest rate, time, interest, principal

6. Complete the table.

	Principal ·	rate ·	time =	interest
Account 1	$2,500	5%	2 yr	
Account 2	$15,000	4.8%	1 yr	

7. Complete the table to find how far light and sound travel in 60 seconds. (*Hint:* mi/sec means miles per second.)

	Rate	· time =	distance
Light	186,282 mi/sec	60 sec	
Sound	1,088 ft/sec	60 sec	

8. Determine which concept (perimeter, area, or volume) should be used to find each of the following. Then determine which unit of measurement, ft, ft^2, or ft^3, would be appropriate.

   a. The amount of storage in a freezer

   b. The amount of ground covered by a sleeping bag lying on the floor

   c. The distance around a dance floor

NOTATION

Complete the step.

9. Solve $Ax + By = C$ for y.

$$Ax + By = C$$
$$Ax + By - \boxed{} = C - \boxed{}$$
$$By = C - Ax$$
$$\frac{By}{\boxed{}} = \frac{C - Ax}{\boxed{}}$$
$$y = \frac{C - Ax}{\boxed{}}$$

10. a. Approximate 98π to the nearest hundredth.

   b. In the formula $V = \pi r^2 h$, what does r represent? What does h represent?

   c. What does 45°C mean?

   d. What does 15°F mean?

GUIDED PRACTICE

Use a formula to solve each problem. **See Example 1.**

11. HOLLYWOOD As of 2006, the movie *Titanic* had brought in $1,835 million worldwide and made a gross profit of $1,595 million. What did it cost to make the movie?

12. VALENTINE'S DAY Find the markup on a dozen roses if a florist buys them wholesale for $12.95 and sells them for $47.50.

13. SERVICE CLUBS After expenses of $55.15 were paid, a Rotary Club donated $875.85 in proceeds from a pancake breakfast to a local health clinic. How much did the pancake breakfast gross?

14. NEW CARS The factory invoice for a minivan shows that the dealer paid $16,264.55 for the vehicle. If the sticker price of the van is $18,202, how much over factory invoice is the sticker price?

See Example 2.

15. ENTREPRENEURS To start a mobile dog-grooming service, a woman borrowed $2,500. If the loan was for 2 years and the amount of interest was $175, what simple interest rate was she charged?

16. SAVINGS A man deposited $5,000 in a credit union paying 6% simple interest. How long will the money have to be left on deposit to earn $6,000 in interest?

17. LOANS A student borrowed some money from his father at 2% simple interest to buy a car. If he paid his father $360 in interest after 3 years, how much did he borrow?

18. BANKING Three years after opening an account that paid simple interest of 6.45% annually, a depositor withdrew the $3,483 in interest earned. How much money was left in the account?

See Example 3.

19. SWIMMING In 1930, a man swam down the Mississippi River from Minneapolis to New Orleans, a total of 1,826 miles. He was in the water for 742 hours. To the nearest tenth, what was his average swimming rate?

20. PARADES Rose Parade floats travel down the 5.5-mile-long parade route at a rate of 2.5 mph. How long will it take a float to complete the route if there are no delays?

21. HOT-AIR BALLOONS If a hot-air balloon travels at an average of 37 mph, how long will it take to fly 166.5 miles?

22. AIR TRAVEL An airplane flew from Chicago to San Francisco in 3.75 hours. If the cities are 1,950 miles apart, what was the average speed of the plane?

See Example 4.

23. FRYING FOODS One of the most popular cookbooks in U.S. history, *The Joy of Cooking,* recommends frying foods at $365°F$ for best results. Convert this to degrees Celsius.

24. FREEZING POINTS Saltwater has a much lower freezing point than freshwater does. For saltwater that is as saturated as much it can possibly get (23.3% salt by weight), the freezing point is $-5.8°F$. Convert this to degrees Celsius.

25. BIOLOGY Cryobiologists freeze living matter to preserve it for future use. They can work with temperatures as low as $-270°C$. Change this to degrees Fahrenheit.

26. METALLURGY Change $2,212°C$, the temperature at which silver boils, to degrees Fahrenheit. Round to the nearest degree.

See Examples 5–7. *If you do not have a calculator, use 3.14 as an approximation of π. Answers may vary slightly depending on which approximation of π is used.*

27. ENERGY SAVINGS One hundred inches of foam weather stripping tape was placed around the perimeter of a rectangular-shaped window. If the length of the window is 30 inches, what is its width?

28. RUGS Find the amount of floor area covered by a circular throw rug that has a radius of 15 inches. Round to the nearest square inch.

29. STRAWS Find the volume of a 150 millimeter-long drinking straw that has an inside diameter of 4 millimeters. Round to the nearest cubic millimeter.

30. RUBBER BANDS The world's largest rubber band ball is $5\frac{1}{2}$ ft tall and was made in 2006 by Steve Milton of Eugene, Oregon. Find the volume of the ball. Round to the nearest cubic foot. $\left(\textit{Hint:}\ \text{The formula for the volume of a sphere is } V = \frac{4}{3}\pi r^3.\right)$

Solve each formula for the specified variable. See Example 8.

31. $r = c + m$ for c **32.** $p = r - c$ for c

33. $P = a + b + c$ for b **34.** $a + b + c = 180$ for a

Solve each formula for the specified variable. See Example 9.

35. $E = IR$ for R **36.** $d = rt$ for t

37. $V = lwh$ for l **38.** $I = Prt$ for r

39. $C = 2\pi r$ for r **40.** $V = \pi r^2 h$ for h

41. $V = \frac{1}{3}Bh$ for h **42.** $C = \frac{1}{7}Rt$ for R

43. $w = \dfrac{s}{f}$ for f **44.** $P = \dfrac{ab}{c}$ for c

Solve each formula for the specified variable. See Examples 10 and 11.

45. $T = 2r + 2t$ for r **46.** $y = mx + b$ for x

47. $Ax + By = C$ for x **48.** $A = P + Prt$ for t

49. $K = \frac{1}{2}mv^2$ for m **50.** $V = \frac{1}{3}\pi r^2 h$ for h

51. $A = \dfrac{a + b + c}{3}$ for c **52.** $x = \dfrac{a + b}{2}$ for b

53. $2E = \dfrac{T - t}{9}$ for t **54.** $D = \dfrac{C - s}{n}$ for s

Solve each equation for the specified variable (or expression). See Example 12.

55. $s = 4\pi r^2$ for r^2 **56.** $E = mc^2$ for c^2

57. $Kg = \dfrac{wv^2}{2}$ for v^2 **58.** $c^2 = a^2 + b^2$ for a^2

▌**TRY IT YOURSELF**

Solve each equation for the specified variable (or expression).

59. $V = \frac{4}{3}\pi r^3$ for r^3 **60.** $A = \dfrac{\pi r^2 S}{360}$ for r^2

61. $\dfrac{M}{2} - 9.9 = 2.1B$ for M **62.** $\dfrac{G}{0.5} + 16r = -8t$ for G

63. $S = 2\pi rh + 2\pi r^2$ for h **64.** $c = bn + 16t^2$ for t^2

65. $3x + y = 9$ for y **66.** $-5x + y = 4$ for y

67. $-x + 3y = 9$ for y **68.** $5y - x = 25$ for y

69. $4y + 16 = -3x$ for y **70.** $6y + 12 = -5x$ for y

71. $A = \frac{1}{2}h(b + d)$ for b

72. $C = \frac{1}{4}s(t - d)$ for t

73. $\frac{7}{8}c + w = 9$ for c **74.** $\frac{3}{4}m - t = 5b$ for m

APPLICATIONS

75. AUTOMOTIVE SERVICE TECHNICIAN If your automobile engine is making a knocking sound, a service technician will probably tell you that the octane rating of the gasoline that you are using is too low. Octane rating numbers are printed on the yellow decals on gas pumps. The formula used to calculate them is

© Jeremy Hardie/The Image Bank/Getty Images

$$\text{Pump octane number} = \frac{(R + M)}{2}$$

where R is the *research octane number,* which is determined with a test engine running at a low speed and M is the *motor octane number,* which is determined with a test engine running at a higher speed. Calculate the octane rating for the following three grades of gasoline.

Gasoline grade	R	M	Octane rating
Unleaded	92	82	
Unleaded plus	95	83	
Premium	97	85	

76. PROPERTIES OF WATER The boiling point and the freezing point of water are to be given in both degrees Celsius and degrees Fahrenheit on the thermometer. Find the missing degree measures.

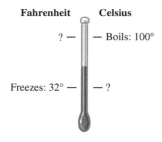

Fahrenheit   Celsius

? —   — Boils: 100°

Freezes: 32° —   — ?

77. AVON PRODUCTS Complete the financial statement.

Income statement (dollar amounts in millions)	Quarter ending Sep 04	Quarter ending Sep 05
Revenue	1,806.2	1,886.0
Cost of goods sold	1,543.4	1,638.9
Operating profit		

Source: Avon Products, Inc.

78. CREDIT CARDS The finance charge that a student pays on his credit card is 19.8% APR (annual percentage rate). Determine the finance charges (interest) the student would have to pay if the account's average balance for the year was $2,500.

79. CAMPERS The perimeter of the window of the camper shell is 140 in. Find the length of one of the shorter sides of the window.

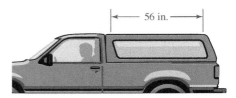

← 56 in. →

80. FLAGS The flag of Eritrea, a country in east Africa, is shown. The perimeter of the flag is 160 inches.

    a. What is the width of the flag?

← 48 in. →

    b. What is the area of the red triangular region of the flag?

81. KITES 650 in.^{2} of nylon cloth were used to make the kite shown. If its height is 26 inches, what is the wingspan?

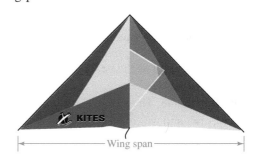

← Wing span →

82. MEMORIALS The Vietnam Veterans Memorial is a black granite wall recognizing the more than 58,000 Americans who lost their lives or remain missing. Find the total area of the two triangular-shaped surfaces on which the names are inscribed.

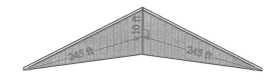

10 ft   245 ft   245 ft

83.

Dietitians often calculate a patient's BMI (Body Mass Index) to screen for weight categories that may lead to health problems. BMI is a number that is calculated from one's weight and height. It is an indication of a person's total body weight that comes from fat. The formula for BMI, as it appears in dietary textbooks, is:

$$\text{BMI} = \frac{\text{weight (lb)} \cdot 703}{\text{height}^2 (\text{in.}^2)}$$

Solve the formula for weight.

84. SURFACE AREA To find the amount of tin needed to make the coffee can shown below, we use the formula for the surface area of a right circular cylinder, $A = 2\pi r^2 + 2\pi rh$. Solve the formula for h.

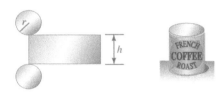

85. ICE CREAM If the two equal-sized scoops of ice cream melt completely into the cone, will they overflow the cone?

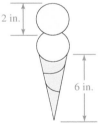

86. GEOGRAPHY The circumference of the Earth is about 25,000 miles. Find its diameter to the nearest mile.

87. HOCKEY A goal is scored in hockey when the puck, a vulcanized rubber disk 2.5 cm (1 in.) thick and 7.6 cm (3 in.) in diameter, is driven into the opponent's goal. Find the volume of a puck in cubic centimeters and cubic inches. Round to the nearest tenth.

88. ELECTRONICS The illustration in the next column is a diagram of a resistor connected to a voltage source of 60 volts. As a result, the resistor loses power in the form

of heat. The power P lost when a voltage E is placed across a resistance R (in ohms) is given by the formula

$$P = \frac{E^2}{R}$$

Solve for R. If P is 4.8 watts and E is 60 volts, find R.

89. WORLD HISTORY The Inca Empire (1438–1533) was centered in what is now called Peru. A special feature of Inca architecture was the trapezoid-shaped windows and doorways. A standard Inca window was 70 cm (centimeters) high, 50 cm at the base and 40 cm at the top. Find the area of a window opening. (*Hint:* The formula for the area of a trapezoid is $A = \frac{1}{2}(\text{height})(\text{upperbase} + \text{lowerbase})$.)

90. HAMSTER HABITATS Find the amount of space in the tube.

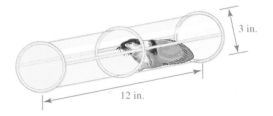

91. TIRES The road surface footprint of a sport truck tire is approximately rectangular. If the area of the footprint is 45 in.^{2}, about how wide is the tire?

$7\frac{1}{2}$ in.

92. SOFTBALL The strike zone in fast-pitch softball is between the batter's armpit and the top of her knees, as shown. If the area of the strike zone for this batter is 442 in.^{2}, what is the width of home plate?

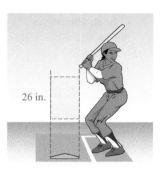

26 in.

93. FIREWOOD The cord of wood shown occupies a volume of 128 ft^3. How long is the stack?

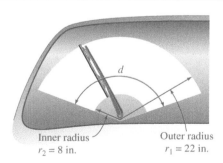

4 ft

4 ft

94. ALUMINUM FOIL Find the number of *square feet* of aluminum foil on a roll if the dimensions printed on the box are $8\frac{1}{3}$ yards $\times$ 12 inches.

95. WIPER DESIGN The area cleaned by the windshield wiper shown below is given by the formula

$$A = \frac{d\pi(r_1^2 - r_2^2)}{360}$$

Solve the equation for d and use your result to find the number of degrees d the wiper arm must swing for each type of vehicle. Round to the nearest degree.

Vehicle	Area cleaned	d (deg)
Luxury car	513 in.^{2}	
Sport utility vehicle	586 in.^{2}	

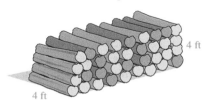

d

Inner radius
$r_2 = 8$ in.

Outer radius
$r_1 = 22$ in.

96. PYRAMIDS The Great Pyramid at Giza in northern Egypt as shown in the next column, is one of the most famous works of architecture in the world. Find its volume to the nearest cubic foot.

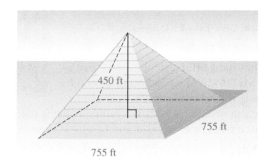

450 ft

755 ft

755 ft

97. COST OF ELECTRICITY The cost of electricity in a city is given by the formula $C = 0.07n + 6.50$, where C is the cost in dollars and n is the number of kilowatt hours used. Solve for n. Then find the number of kilowatt hours used each month by a homeowner whose checks to pay the monthly electric bills are: $49.97, $76.50, and $125.

98. COST OF WATER A monthly water bill in a certain city is calculated by using the formula $n = \frac{5{,}000C - 17{,}500}{6}$, where n is the number of gallons used and C is the monthly cost in dollars. Solve for C and compute the bill for quantities of 500, 1,200, and 2,500 gallons.

99. PULLEYS The approximate length L of a belt joining two pulleys of radii r and R feet with centers D feet apart is given by the formula $L = 2D + 3.25(r + R)$. Solve the formula for D.

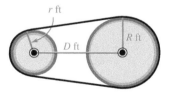

r ft

D ft

R ft

100. THERMODYNAMICS The Gibbs free-energy function is given by $G = U - TS + pV$. Solve this formula for the pressure p.

WRITING

101. After solving $A = B + C + D$ for B, a student compared her answer with that at the back of the textbook. Could this problem have two different-looking answers? Explain why or why not.

Student's answer: $B = A - C - D$
Book's answer: $B = A - D - C$

102. A student solved $x + 5c = 3c + a$ for c. His answer was $c = \frac{3c + a - x}{5}$ for c. Explain why the equation is not solved for c.

103. Explain the difference between what perimeter measures and what area measures.

104. Explain the error made below.

$$y = \frac{3x + \overset{1}{2}}{\underset{1}{2}}$$

SECTION **4.6**
Applications Introduction Let $x =$

In Sections 4.6 and 4.7, we will use a six-step problem-solving strategy to solve a wide variety of application problems. With this method, we **analyze** the problem by reading it carefully and **assign** a variable to represent an unknown value in the problem. Then we translate the words of the problem to **form** an equation that mathematically describes the situation. Finally, we **solve** the equation to find the value of the variable, **state** the conclusion clearly, and **check** the result.

In problems 1 through 8, you are to perform only Steps 1 and 2 of the problem-solving strategy. Begin by reading each problem carefully. Circle what you are asked to find. Then let x represent the unknown quantity. You do not have to finish the solution process. The first problem is done for you.

1. AUTO REPAIRS A woman paid $29 less to have her car repaired at a muffler shop than she would have paid at a gas station. If she paid $190 at the muffler shop, what was the gas station going to charge her?

Let $x =$ the amount that the gas station was going to charge her (in dollars)

2. RIDING BUSES A man had to wait 20 minutes for a bus today. Three days ago, he had to wait 15 minutes longer than he did today, because several buses passed by without stopping. How long did he wait three days ago?

3. LIFE SPAN The average life span of an Amazon parrot is 104 years. That is thirteen times longer than the average life span of a Guinea pig. Find the average life span of a Guinea pig. (Source: petdoc.com)

4. SPEED READING An advertisement for a speed reading program claimed that successful completion of the course could triple a person's reading rate. After taking the course, Alicia can now read 399 words per minute. If the company's claims are true, what was her reading rate before taking the course?

5. ANTIQUES A woman purchases 4 antique spoons each year. She now owns 56 spoons. In how many years will she have 100 spoons in her collection?

6. COMMERCIALS For the typical "one-hour" prime-time television slot, the number of minutes of commercials is $\frac{3}{7}$ of the number of minutes of the actual program. Determine how many minutes of the program are shown in that one hour.

7. **PEST CONTROL** How much of a 4% pesticide solution must be added to 20 gallons of a 12% pesticide solution to dilute it to a 10% solution?

8. **COLORADO** The state of Colorado is approzimately rectangular-shaped with perimeter 1,320 miles, Find the width (north to south), if the length is 100 miles longer than the width.

9. **TEA** How many pounds of green tea, worth $40 a pound, should be mixed with herbal tea, worth $50 a pound, to produce 20 pounds of a blend worth $42 a pound?

10. **LOANS** A student plans to pay back a $600 loan with monthly payments of $30. After how many payments will the amount she owes be reduced to $420?

In problems 11 through 14, read the problem carefully. Circle what you are asked to find. Then draw a picture of the situation. Label the unknown value(s) with a variable or algebraic expression. You do not have to finish the solution process. The first problem is done for you.

11. **GEOMETRY** If one base angle of an isosceles triangle measures 70°, (what is the measure of the vertex angle?)

12. **GEOMETRY** If the vertex angle of an isosceles triangle measures 85°, what is the measure of each base angle?

13. **TENNIS** The perimeter of a regulation singles tennis court is 201 feet and the length is 3 feet less than three times the width. What is the width of the court?

14. **MOUNTAIN BICYCLES** For the bicycle frame shown, the angle that the horizontal crossbar makes with the seat support is 15° less than twice the angle at the steering column. The angle at the pedal gear is 25° more than the angle at the steering column. Find the measure of the angle at the stering column.

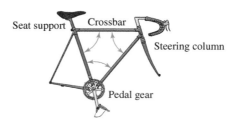

15. CARPENTRY A 24-foot long board is cut into two pieces, one three times as long as the other. Find the length of the shorter piece.

16. PLUMBING A 42-inch long piece of pipe is cut into three sections. The longest section is twice as long as the shortest section, and the middle-sized section is 2 inches longer than the shortest. Find the length of the shortest section.

SECTION 4.6
Problem Solving

Objectives

1 Apply the steps of a problem-solving strategy.

2 Solve consecutive integer problems.

3 Solve geometry problems.

ARE YOU READY?

The following problems review some basic skills that are needed to solve the application problems in this section.

1. Simplify: $x + x + 1 + 2x + 3$
2. If $x = 8$, find $6x + 1$.
3. If staplers cost $4.35 each, what is the cost of 9 staplers?
4. Simplify: $x - 0.72x$
5. What is the formula for the perimeter of a rectangle?
6. What is the sum of the measures of the angles of a triangle?
7. Translate to symbols: *8 less than twice a number x*
8. Write 6% as a decimal.

In this section, you will see that algebra is a powerful tool that can be used to solve a wide variety of real-world problems.

1 Apply the steps of a problem-solving strategy.

To become a good problem solver, you need a plan to follow, such as the following five-step strategy.

> *The Language of Algebra*   A **strategy** is a careful plan or method. For example, a businessman might develop a new advertising *strategy* to increase sales or a long distance runner might have a *strategy* to win a marathon.

Strategy for Problem Solving

1. **Analyze the problem** by reading it carefully to understand the given facts. What information is given? What are you asked to find? What vocabulary is given? Often, a diagram or table will help you understand the facts of the problem.

2. **Assign a variable** to represent an unknown value in the problem. This means, in most cases, to let $x =$ what you are asked to find. If there are other unknown values, represent each of them using an algebraic expression that involves the variable.

3. **Form an equation** by translating the words of the problem into mathematical symbols.

4. **Solve the equation** formed in step 3.

5. **State the conclusion clearly.** Be sure to include the units (such as feet, seconds, or pounds) in your answer.

6. **Check the result** using the original wording of the problem, not the equation that was formed in step 3.

Self Check 1

The Mountain-Bay State Park Bike Trail in Northeast Wisconsin is 76 miles long. A couple rode the trail in four days. Each day they rode 2 miles more than the previous day. How many miles did they ride each day?

Now Try **Problem 18**

EXAMPLE 1   *California Coastline*

The first part of California's magnificent 17-Mile Drive begins at the Pacific Grove entrance and continues to Seal Rock. It is 1 mile longer than the second part of the drive, which extends from Seal Rock to the Lone Cypress. The final part of the tour winds through the Monterey Peninsula, eventually returning to the entrance. This part of the drive is 1 mile longer than four times the length of the second part. How long is each part of 17-Mile Drive?

© Visions of America, LLC/Alamy

Analyze The drive is composed of three parts. We need to find the length of each part. We can straighten out the winding 17-Mile Drive and model it with a line segment.

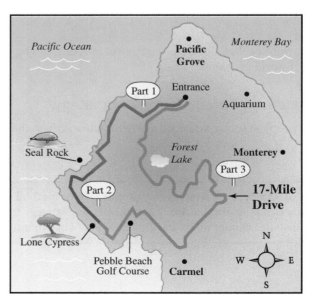

Assign Since the lengths of the first part and of the third part of the drive are related to the length of the second part, we will let x represent the length of that part. We then express the other lengths in terms of x. Let

x = the length of the second part of the drive

$x + 1$ = the length of the first part of the drive

$4x + 1$ = the length of the third part of the drive

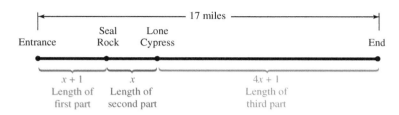

Form The sum of the lengths of the three parts must be 17 miles.

The length of part 1	plus	the length of part 2	plus	the length of part 3	equals	the total length.
$x + 1$	+	x	+	$4x + 1$	=	17

Solve

$$x + 1 + x + 4x + 1 = 17$$

$6x + 2 = 17$ Combine like terms: x + x + 4x = 6x and 1 + 1 = 2.

$6x = 15$ To undo the addition of 2, subtract 2 from both sides.

$\dfrac{6x}{6} = \dfrac{15}{6}$ To isolate x, undo the multiplication by 6 by dividing both sides by 6.

$x = 2.5$ Do the divisions.

Recall that x represents the length of the second part of the drive. To find the lengths of the first and third parts, we evaluate $x + 1$ and $4x + 1$ for $x = 2.5$.

First part of drive

$x + 1 = 2.5 + 1$

$= 3.5$

Third part of drive

$4x + 1 = 4(2.5) + 1$ Substitute 2.5 for x.

$= 11$

State The first part of the drive is 3.5 miles long, the second part is 2.5 miles long, and the third part is 11 miles long.

Check Since 3.5 mi + 2.5 mi + 11 mi = 17 mi, the answers check. ∎

EXAMPLE 2 *Computer Logos* A trucking company had their logo embroidered on the front of baseball caps. They were charged $8.90 per hat plus a one-time setup fee of $25. If the project cost $559, how many hats were embroidered?

Analyze

- It cost $8.90 to have a logo embroidered on a hat.
- The setup charge was $25.
- The project cost $559.
- We are to find the number of hats that were embroidered.

Self Check 2

A school club had their motto screenprinted on the front of T-shirts. They were charged $5 per shirt plus a one-time setup fee of $20. If the project cost $255, how many T-shirts were printed?

Now Try **Problem 25**

Assign Let $x =$ the number of hats that were embroidered. If x hats are embroidered, at a cost of $8.90 per hat, the cost to embroider all of the hats is $x \cdot \$8.90$ or $\$8.90x$.

Form Now we translate the words of the problem into an equation.

The cost to embroider on hat	times	the number of hats	plus	the setup charge	equals	the total cost.
8.90	·	x	+	25	=	559

Solve

$$8.90x + 25 = 559$$

$$8.90x = 534 \qquad \text{To undo the addition of 25, subtract 25 from both sides.}$$

$$\frac{8.90x}{8.90} = \frac{534}{8.90} \qquad \text{To isolate x, undo the multiplication by 8.90 by dividing both sides by 8.90.}$$

$$x = 60 \qquad \text{Do the divisions.}$$

State The company had 60 hats embroidered.

Check The cost to embroider 60 hats is $60(\$8.90) = \$534$. When the $25 setup charge is added, we get $\$534 + \$25 = \$559$. The answer checks.

> **Success Tip** The *Form* step is often the hardest. To help, write a **verbal model** of the situation (shown here in blue) and then translate it into an equation.

Self Check 3

A farmer is going to sell one of his Black Angus cattle at an auction and would like to make $2,597 after paying a 6% commission to the auctioneer. For what selling price will the farmer make this amount of money?

Now Try **Problem 31**

EXAMPLE 3 *Auctions* A classic car owner is going to sell his 1960 Chevy Impala at an auction. He wants to make $46,000 after paying an 8% commission to the auctioneer. For what selling price (called the "hammer price") will the car owner make this amount of money?

Analyze When the commission is subtracted from the selling price of the car, the owner wants to have $46,000 left.

Assign Let $x =$ the selling price of the car. The amount of the commission is 8% of x, or $0.08x$.

Form Now we translate the words of the problem to an equation.

The selling price of the car	minus	the auctioneer's commission	should be	$46,000.
x	−	0.08x	=	46,000

Solve

$$x - 0.08x = 46,000$$

$$0.92x = 46,000 \qquad \text{Combine like terms: 1.00x − 0.08x = 0.92x.}$$

$$\frac{0.92x}{0.92} = \frac{46,000}{0.92} \qquad \text{To isolate x, undo the multiplication by 0.92 by dividing both sides by 0.92.}$$

$$x = 50,000 \qquad \text{Do the divisions.}$$

State The owner will make $46,000 if the car sells for $50,000.

Check An 8% commission on $50,000 is 0.08($50,000) = $4,000. The owner will keep $50,000 − $4,000 = $46,000. The answer checks. ∎

2 Solve consecutive integer problems.

Integers that follow one another, such as 15 and 16, are called **consecutive integers.** They are 1 unit apart. **Consecutive even integers** are even integers that differ by 2 units, such as 12 and 14. Similarly, **consecutive odd integers** differ by 2 units, such as 9 and 11. When solving consecutive integer problems, if we let x = the first integer, then

- two consecutive integers are x and $x + 1$
- two consecutive even integers are x and $x + 2$
- two consecutive odd integers are x and $x + 2$

EXAMPLE 4 *U.S. History* The year George Washington was chosen president and the year the Bill of Rights went into effect are consecutive odd integers whose sum is 3,580. Find the years.

Analyze We need to find two consecutive odd integers whose sum is 3,580. From history, we know that Washington was elected president first and the Bill of Rights went into effect later.

Assign Let x = the first odd integer (the date when Washington was chosen president). The next odd integer is 2 *greater than* x, therefore $x + 2$ = the next larger odd integer (the date when the Bill of Rights went into effect).

Form

The first odd integer	plus	the second odd integer	is	3,580.
x	+	$x + 2$	=	3,580

Solve

$x + x + 2 = 3,580$

$2x + 2 = 3,580$ Combine like terms: $x + x = 2x$.

$2x = 3,578$ To undo the addition of 2, subtract 2 from both sides.

$x = 1,789$ To isolate x, undo the multiplication by 2 by dividing both sides by 2.

State George Washington was chosen president in the year 1789. The Bill of Rights went into effect in $1789 + 2 = 1791$.

Check 1789 and 1791 are consecutive odd integers whose sum is $1789 + 1791 = 3,580$. The answers check. ∎

> *The Language of Algebra* *Consecutive* means following one after the other in order. Elton John holds the record for the most *consecutive* years with a song on the Top 50 music chart: 31 years (1970 to 2000).

Self Check 4

The definitions of the words *little* and *lobby* are on back-to-back pages in a dictionary. If the sum of the page numbers is 1,159, on what page can the definition of *little* be found?

Now Try **Problem 39**

3 Solve geometry problems.

Self Check 5

A rectangular counter for the customer service department of a store is 6 feet longer than it is wide. If the perimeter is 32 feet, find the outside dimensions of the counter.

Now Try **Problem 45**

EXAMPLE 5   *Crime Scenes*   Police used 400 feet of yellow tape to fence off a rectangular-shaped lot for an investigation. Fifty less feet of tape was used for each width as for each length. Find the dimensions of the lot.

Analyze Since the yellow tape surrounded the lot, the concept of perimeter applies. Recall that the formula for the perimeter of a rectangle is $P = 2l + 2w$. We also know that the width of the lot is 50 feet less than the length.

Assign Since the width of the lot is given in terms of the length, we let l = the length of the lot. Then $l - 50$ = the width.

Form Using the perimeter formula, we have:

2	times	the length	plus	2	times	the width	is	the perimeter.
2	·	l	+	2	·	$(l - 50)$	=	400

Solve

$$2l + 2(l - 50) = 400$$ Write the parentheses so that the entire expression $l - 50$ is multiplied by 2.

$$2l + 2l - 100 = 400$$ Distribute the multiplication by 2.

$$4l - 100 = 400$$ Combine like terms: $2l + 2l = 4l$.

$$4l = 500$$ To undo the subtraction of 100, add 100 to both sides.

$$l = 125$$ To isolate l, undo the multiplication by 4 by dividing both sides by 4.

State The length of the lot is 125 feet and width is $125 - 50 = 75$ feet.

Check The width (75 feet) is 50 less than the length (125 feet). The perimeter of the lot is $2(125) + 2(75) = 250 + 150 = 400$ feet. The answers check.

Self Check 6

The perimeter of an isosceles triangle is 32 cm. If the base is 8 cm, find the length of each remaining side.

Now Try **Problem 49**

EXAMPLE 6   *Isosceles Triangles*   If the vertex angle of an isosceles triangle is 56°, find the measure of each base angle.

Analyze An **isosceles triangle** has two sides of equal length, which meet to form the **vertex angle.** In this case, the measurement of the vertex angle is 56°. We can sketch the triangle as shown. The **base angles** opposite the equal sides are also equal. We need to find their measure.

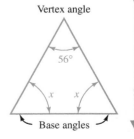

Assign If we let x = the measure of one base angle, the measure of the other base angle is also x. Since the sum of the angles of any triangle is 180°, the sum of the base angles and the vertex angle is 180°.

Form We can use this fact to form the equation.

One base angle	plus	the other base angle	plus	the vertex angle	is	180°.
x	$+$	x	$+$	56	$=$	180

Solve

$x + x + 56 = 180$

$2x + 56 = 180$ Combine like terms: x + x = 2x.

$2x = 124$ To undo the addition of 56, subtract 56 from both sides.

$x = 62$ To isolate x, undo the multiplication by 2 by dividing both sides by 2.

State The measure of each base angle is 62°.

Check Since $62° + 62° + 56° = 180°$, the answer checks.

ANSWERS TO SELF CHECKS

1. 16 mi, 18 mi, 20 mi, 22 mi   **2.** 47   **3.** \$2,762.77   **4.** 579   **5.** 5 ft by 11 ft   **6.** 12 cm, 12 cm

---

SECTION 4.6   STUDY SET

VOCABULARY

Fill in the blanks.

1. Integers that follow one another, such as 7 and 8, are called _____ integers.

2. An _____ triangle is a triangle with two sides of the same length.

3. The equal sides of an isosceles triangle meet to form the _____ angle. The angles opposite the equal sides are called _____ angles, and they have equal measures.

4. When asked to find the dimensions of a rectangle, we are to find its _____ and _____.

CONCEPTS

5. A 17-foot pipe is cut into three sections. The longest section is three times as long as the shortest, and the middle-sized section is 2 feet longer than the shortest. Complete the diagram.

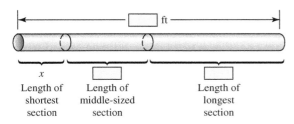

| Length of shortest section | Length of middle-sized section | Length of longest section |

6. It costs \$28 per hour to rent a trailer. Write an expression that represents the cost to rent the trailer for x hours.

7. A realtor is paid a 3% commission on the sale of a house. Write an expression that represents the amount of the commission if a house sells for \$$x$.

8. The perimeter of the rectangle is 15 feet. Fill in the blanks: $2\Big(\quad\Big) + 2x =$

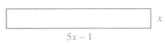

$5x - 1$

9. What is the sum of the measures of the angles of any triangle?

10. What is x?

NOTATION

11. a. If x represents an integer, write an expression for the next largest integer.

b. If *x* represents an odd integer, write an expression for the next largest odd integer.

12. What does 45° mean?

GUIDED PRACTICE

See Examples 1–3.

13. A 12-foot board has been cut into two sections, one twice as long as the other. How long is each section?

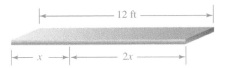

14. The robotic arm will extend a total distance of 18 feet. Find the length of each section.

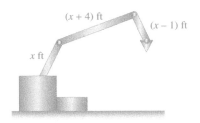

15. NATIONAL PARKS The Great Smoky Mountains National Park covers a total of 520,000 acres in the states of Tennessee and North Carolina. The number of acres in Tennessee is 32,000 less that in North Carolina. How many acres of the park are in North Carolina?

16. TV HISTORY Andy Griffith is one of America's all-time favorite television stars. In *The Andy Griffith Show*, which first aired in the 1960's, Griffith played a sheriff in the fictional community of Mayberry, North Carolina. From 1986-1995, he played a folksy defense lawyer in the legal drama *Matlock*. The total number of episodes of these two television shows was 444. If there were 54 more episodes of the *The Andy Griffith Show* than *Matlock,* how many episodes of each were made?

17. NATIONAL PARKS The Natchez Trace Parkway is a historical 444-mile route from Natchez, Mississippi, to Nashville, Tennessee. A couple drove the Trace in four days. Each day they drove 6 miles more than the previous day. How many miles did they drive each day?

18. TOURING A rock group plans to travel for a total of 38 weeks, making three concert stops. They will be in Japan for 4 more weeks than they will be in Australia. Their stay in Sweden will be 2 weeks shorter than that in Australia. How many weeks will they be in each country?

19. SOLAR HEATING Refer to the illustration. One solar panel is 3.4 feet wider than the other. Find the width of each panel.

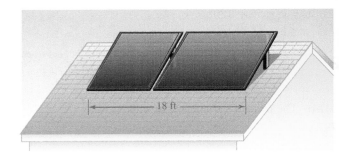

20. ACCOUNTING Determine the 2010 income of Aeropostale Inc. for each quarter from the data in the graph below.

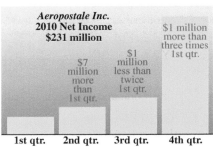

Source: moneycentral.msn.com

21. IPHONE APPS A student spent a total of $52.97 on the purchase of three applications in the Apps Store on his iPhone. *Call of Duty: World at War: Zombies II* cost $7 more than *Guitar Hero*, and *Tom Tom USA* cost $4.11 more than twelve times *Guitar Hero*. Find the cost of each application.

22. WATER USAGE It takes about 3.8 times more gallons of water to produce one pound of grain-fed beef than it does to produce one pound of grain-fed chicken. If a combined total of 3,135 gallons of water are needed to produce one pound of each meat, how many gallons does it take to produce one pound of chicken? How many gallons does it take to produce one pound of beef? (Source: The Sierra Club: *The True Cost of Food*)

23. COUNTING CALORIES A slice of pie with a scoop of ice cream has 850 calories. The calories in the pie alone are 100 more than twice the calories in the ice cream alone. How many calories are in each food?

24. WASTE DISPOSAL Two tanks hold a total of 45 gallons of a toxic solvent. One tank holds 6 gallons more than twice the amount in the other. How many gallons does each tank hold?

25. CONCERTS The fee to rent a concert hall is $2,250 plus $150 per hour to pay for the support staff. For how many hours can an orchestra rent the hall and stay within a budget of $3,300?

26. TRUCK MECHANICS An engine repair cost a truck owner $1,185 in parts and labor. If the parts were $690 and the mechanic charged $45 per hour, how many hours did the repair take?

27. FIELD TRIPS It costs a school $65 a day plus $0.25 per mile to rent a 15-passenger van. If the van is rented for two days, how many miles can be driven on a $275 budget?

28. DECORATIONS A party supply store charges a set-up fee of $80 plus 35¢ per balloon to make a balloon arch. A business has $150 to spend on decorations for their grand opening. How many balloons can they have in the arch? (*Hint:* 35¢ = $0.35.)

29. TUTORING High school students enrolling in a private tutoring program must first take a placement test (cost $25) before receiving tutoring (cost $18.75 per hour). If a family has set aside $400 to get their child extra help, how many hours of tutoring can they afford?

30. DATA CONVERSION The *Books2Bytes* service converts old print books to Microsoft Word electronic files for $20 per book plus $2.25 per page. If it cost $1,201.25 to convert a novel, how many pages did the novel have?

31. CATTLE AUCTIONS A cattle rancher is going to sell one of his prize bulls at an auction and would like to make $45,500 after paying a 9% commission to the auctioneer. For what selling price will the rancher make this amount of money?

32. LISTING PRICE At what price should a home be listed if the owner wants to make $567,000 on its sale after paying a 5.5% real estate commission?

33. SAVINGS ACCOUNTS The balance in a savings account grew by 5% in one year, to $5,512.50. What was the balance at the beginning of the year?

34. ALUMINUM CANS Today's aluminum cans are much thinner and lighter than those of the past. From 1972 to 2010, the number of empty cans produced from one pound of aluminum has increased by about 45%. If 32 cans could be produced from one pound of aluminum in 2010, how many cans could be produced from one pound of aluminum in 1972? Round to the nearest can. (Source: cancentral.com)

35. SELLING USED CLOTHING A *consignment shop* accepts an item of clothing that no longer fits (or one you have grown tired of) and sells it for you. The shop then charges you an agreed on percent of the selling price as their profit. Suppose the owner of a designer wool coat would like to make $210 on its sale at a consignment shop. If there is a $12\frac{1}{2}$% consignment charge, for what price must the coat be sold?

36. FINDER'S FEES A *finder's fee* is an amount of money that is paid to someone who brings people together for business purposes. Suppose the owner of a software company needs to sell it and make $9,950,000 to pay back creditors. If he expects to pay a finder's fee of $\frac{1}{2}$% of the selling price to find a qualified buyer, for what price must the company be sold?

Consecutive integer problems See Example 4.

37. SOCCER Ronaldo of Brazil and Gerd Mueller of Germany rank 1 and 2, respectively, with the most goals scored in World Cup play. The number of goals Ronaldo and Mueller have scored are consecutive integers that total 29. Find the number of goals scored by each man.

38. DICTIONARIES The definitions of the words *job* and *join* are on back-to-back pages in a dictionary. If the sum of those page numbers is 1,411, on what page can the definition of *job* be found?

39. TV HISTORY *Friends* and *Leave It to Beaver* are two of the most popular television shows of all time. The number of episodes of each show are consecutive even integers whose sum is 470. If there are more episodes of *Friends,* how many episodes of each were there?

40. VACATIONS The table shows the amount of paid time off that workers in selected countries are entitled to each year by law. Complete the table. (The numbers of days are listed in descending order.)

Total paid days off	
Country	**Days**
Brazil	41
Greece	
Norway	
U.S.	10

Consecutive odd integers whose sum is 72.

Source: *The World Almanac,* 2012

41. CELEBRITY BIRTHDAYS Selena Gomez, Jennifer Lopez, and Sandra Bullock have birthdays (in that order) on consecutive even-numbered days in July. The sum of the calendar dates of their birthdays is 72. Find each birthday.

42. LOCKS The three numbers of the combination for a lock are consecutive integers, and their sum is 81. Find the combination.

Geometry problems See Examples 5–6.

43. TENNIS The perimeter of a regulation singles tennis court is 210 feet and the length is 3 feet less than three times the width. What are the dimensions of the court?

44. SWIMMING POOLS The seawater Orthlieb Pool in Casablanca, Morocco, is the largest swimming pool in the world. With a perimeter of 1,110 meters, this rectangular-shaped pool is 30 meters longer than 6 times its width. Find its dimensions.

45. ART The *Mona Lisa* was completed by Leonardo da Vinci in 1506. The length of the picture is 11.75 inches shorter than twice the width. If the perimeter of the picture is 102.5 inches, find its dimensions.

46. NEW YORK CITY Central Park, which lies in the middle of Manhattan, is rectangular-shaped and has a 6-mile perimeter. The length is 5 times the width. What are the dimensions of the park?

47. ENGINEERING A truss is in the form of an isosceles triangle. Each of the two equal sides is 4 feet shorter than the third side. If the perimeter is 25 feet, find the lengths of the sides.

48. FIRST AID A sling, shown in the next column, is in the shape of an isosceles triangle with a perimeter of 144 inches. The longest side of the sling is 18 inches longer than either of the other two sides. Find the lengths of each side.

49. TV TOWERS The two guy wires supporting a tower form an isosceles triangle with the ground. Each of the base angles of the triangle is 4 times the third angle (the vertex angle). Find the measure of the vertex angle.

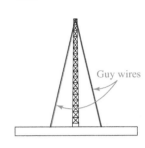

Guy wires

50. CLOTHESLINES A pair of damp jeans are hung in the middle of a clothesline to dry. Find $x°$, the angle that the clothesline makes with the horizontal.

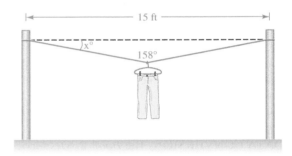

51. MOUNTAIN BICYCLES For the bicycle frame shown in the next column, the angle that the horizontal crossbar makes with the seat support is 15° less than twice the angle at the steering column. The angle at the pedal gear is 25° more than the angle at the steering column. Find these three angle measures.

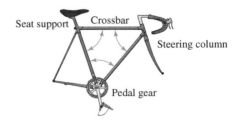

Seat support   Crossbar
Steering column
Pedal gear

52. TRIANGLES The measure of $\angle 1$ (read as angle 1) of a triangle is one-half that of $\angle 2$. The measure of $\angle 3$ is equal to the sum of the measures of $\angle 1$ and $\angle 2$. Find each angle measure.

53. COMPLEMENTARY ANGLES Two angles are called *complementary angles* when the sum of their measures is 90°. Find the measures of the complementary angles shown in the illustration.

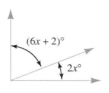
(6x + 2)°
2x°

54. SUPPLEMENTARY ANGLES Two angles are called *supplementary angles* when the sum of their measures is 180°. Find the measures of the supplementary angles shown in the illustration.

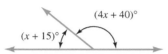
(4x + 40)°
(x + 15)°

55. "LIGHTNING BOLT" In 2010, Usain Bolt of Jamaica held the world record for the 100 meters and the 200 meters sprints. His *maximum stride angle* shown below is 5° less than 1.5 times its supplement. Find his maximum stride angle. You may need to refer to problem 52 to review the geometry involved. (Source: somaxsports.com)

Maximum stride angle

56.

Automotive Service Technician

The *sweep angle* of a windshield wiper arm is 115° as shown below. Find *x* so that the area that is cleared by the wiper is centered on the car's windshield.

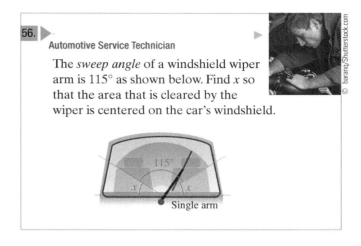
115°
x   x
Single arm

▌WRITING

57. Create a geometry problem that could be answered by solving the equation $2w + 2(w + 5) = 26$.

58. What information do you need to know to answer the following question?

A business rented a copy machine for $85 per month plus 4¢ for every copy made. How many copies can be made each month?

59. Make a list of words and phrases that translate to an equal symbol =.

60. Define the word *strategy*.

SECTION **4.7**
More about Problem Solving

Objectives

1 Solve investment problems.

2 Solve uniform motion problems.

3 Solve liquid mixture problems.

4 Solve dry mixture problems.

5 Solve number-value problems.

ARE YOU READY?

The following problems review basic skills and some formulas that are needed to solve money, motion, and mixture applications.

1. Find the amount of interest earned by $8,000 invested at a 5% annual simple interest rate for 1 year.

2. At 45 miles per hour, how far will a car travel in 3 hours?

3. A 12-gallon mixture of antifreeze and water is 30% antifreeze. How many gallons of the mixture is antifreeze?

4. At $2.45 per pound, what is the value of 8 pounds of ground beef?

5. A couple invested $6,000 of their $20,000 lottery winnings in bonds. How much do they have left to invest in stocks?

6. Multiply: $100(0.03x)$

In this section, we will solve problems that involve money, motion, and mixtures. Tables are a helpful way to organize the information given in these problems.

1 Solve investment problems.

To find the amount of *simple interest I* an investment earns, we use the formula $I = Prt$, where P is the principal (the amount invested), r is the annual interest rate, and t is the time in years.

A student invested $4,200 in certificates of deposit, one at 2% and the other at 3%. Find the amount invested at each rate if the first year combined interest income from the two investments was $102.

Now Try **Problem 17**

EXAMPLE 1 *Paying Tuition* A college student invested the $12,000 inheritance he received and decided to use the annual interest earned to pay his tuition cost of $945. The highest rate offered by a bank at that time was 6% annual simple interest. At this rate, he could not earn the needed $945, so he invested some of the money in a riskier, but more profitable, investment offering a 9% return. How much did he invest at each rate?

Analyze We know that $12,000 was invested for 1 year at two rates: 6% and 9%. We are asked to find the amount invested at each rate so that the total return would be $945.

Assign Let $x =$ the amount invested at 6%. Then $12,000 - x =$ the amount invested at 9%. To organize the facts of the problem, we enter the principal, rate, time, and interest earned in a table.

Step 1: List each investment in a row of the table.

Bank			
Riskier investment			

Step 2: Label the columns using $I = Prt$ reversed and also write Total:.

	P	$\cdot\ r\ \cdot t=$		I
Bank				
Riskier investment				
				Total:

Step 3: Enter the rates, times, and total interest.

	P	$\cdot\ r\ \cdot t=$		I
Bank		0.06	1	
Riskier investment		0.09	1	
				Total: 945

Step 4: Enter each unknown principal.

	P	$\cdot\ r\ \cdot t=$		I
Bank	x	0.06	1	
Riskier investment	$12{,}000 - x$	0.09	1	
				Total: 945

Step 5: In the last column, multiply P, r, and t to obtain expressions for the interest earned.

	P	$\cdot\ r\ \cdot t=$		I	
Bank	x	0.06	1	**0.06x**	←This is x · 0.06 · 1.
Riskier investment	$12{,}000 - x$	0.09	1	**0.09(12,000 − x)**	←
				Total: 945	

Use the information in this ⎯⎤
column to form an equation.

This is $(12{,}000 - x) \cdot 0.09 \cdot 1$.

Form

The interest earned at 6%	plus	the interest earned at 9%	equals	the total interest.
$0.06x$	$+$	$[0.09(12{,}000 - x)]$	$=$	945

Solve

$$0.06x + 0.09(12{,}000 - x) = 945$$

$$100[0.06x + 0.09(12{,}000 - x)] = 100(945)$$ Multiply both sides by 100 to clear the equation of decimals.

$$100(0.06x) + 100(0.09)(12{,}000 - x) = 100(945)$$ Distribute the multiplication by 100.

$$6x + 9(12{,}000 - x) = 94{,}500$$ Do the multiplications by 100.

$$6x + 108{,}000 - 9x = 94{,}500$$ Use the distributive property.

$$-3x + 108{,}000 = 94{,}500$$ Combine like terms.

$$-3x = -13{,}500$$ Subtract 108,000 from both sides.

$$x = 4{,}500$$ To isolate x, divide both sides by −3.

State The student invested \$4,500 at 6% and \$12,000 − \$4,500 = \$7,500 at 9%.

Check The first investment earned 0.06(\$4,500), or \$270. The second earned 0.09(\$7,500), or \$675. Since the total return was \$270 + \$675 = \$945, the answers check.

2 Solve uniform motion problems.

If we know the rate r at which we will be traveling and the time t we will be traveling at that rate, we can find the distance d traveled by using the formula $d = rt$.

Self Check 2

Two search-and-rescue teams leave base at the same time looking for a lost boy. The first team, on foot, heads north at 2 mph, and the other, on horseback, heads south at 4 mph. How long will it take them to search a distance of 21 miles between them?

Now Try **Problem 29**

EXAMPLE 2 *Rescues at Sea* A cargo ship, heading into port, radios the Coast Guard that it is experiencing engine trouble and that its speed has dropped to 3 knots (this is 3 sea miles per hour). Immediately, a Coast Guard cutter leaves port and speeds at a rate of 25 knots directly toward the disabled ship, which is 56 sea miles away. How long will it take the Coast Guard to reach the ship? (Sea miles are also called nautical miles.)

Analyze We know the *rate* of each ship (25 knots and 3 knots), and we know that they must close a *distance* of 56 sea miles between them. We don't know the *time* it will take to do this.

Assign Let $t =$ the time it takes the Coast Guard to reach the cargo ship. During the rescue, the ships don't travel at the same rate, but they do travel for the same amount of time. Therefore, t also represents the travel time for the cargo ship.

We enter the rates, the variable t for each time, and the total distance traveled by the ships (56 sea miles) in the table. To fill in the last column, we use the formula $r \cdot t = d$ twice to find an expression for each distance traveled: $25 \cdot t = 25t$ and $3 \cdot t = 3t$.

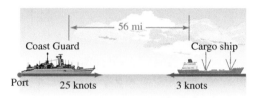

	r	$\cdot$	t	$=$	d
Coast Guard cutter	25		t		$25t$
Cargo ship	3		t		$3t$
				Total:	56

Multiply $r \cdot t$ to obtain an expression for each distance traveled.

Use the information in this column to form an equation.

Form

The distance the cutter travels	plus	the distance the ship travels	equals	the original distance between the ships.
$25t$	$+$	$3t$	$=$	56

Solve

$$25t + 3t = 56$$

$$28t = 56 \qquad \text{Combine like terms: } 25t + 3t = 28t.$$

$$t = \frac{56}{28} \qquad \text{To isolate } t, \text{ divide both sides by 28.}$$

$$t = 2 \qquad \text{Do the division.}$$

State The ships will meet in 2 hours.

Check In 2 hours, the Coast Guard cutter travels $25 \cdot 2 = 50$ sea miles, and the cargo ship travels $3 \cdot 2 = 6$ sea miles. Together, they travel $50 + 6 = 56$ sea miles. Since this is the original distance between the ships, the answer checks.

Success Tip A sketch is helpful when solving uniform motion problems.

EXAMPLE 3   *Concert Tours*   While on tour, a country music star travels by bus. Her musical equipment is carried in a truck. How long will it take her bus, traveling 60 mph, to overtake the truck, traveling at 45 mph, if the truck had a $1\frac{1}{2}$-hour head start to her next concert location?

Analyze   We know the rate of each vehicle (60 mph and 45 mph) and that the truck began the trip $1\frac{1}{2}$ or 1.5 hours earlier than the bus. We need to determine how long it will take the bus to catch up to the truck.

Assign   Let t = the time it takes the bus to overtake the truck. With a 1.5-hour head start, the truck is on the road longer than the bus. Therefore, $t + 1.5$ = the truck's travel time.

We enter each rate and time in the table, and use the formula $r \cdot t = d$ twice to fill in the distance column.

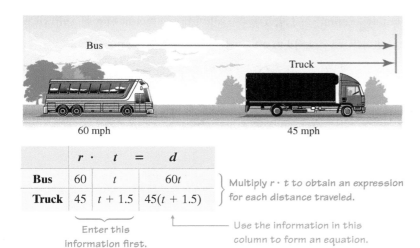

60 mph   45 mph

	r $\cdot$	t =	d
Bus	60	t	$60t$
Truck	45	$t + 1.5$	$45(t + 1.5)$

⎫
⎬ Multiply r · t to obtain an expression
⎭ for each distance traveled.

Enter this information first.

Use the information in this column to form an equation.

Form
When the bus overtakes the truck, they will have traveled the same distance.

The distance traveled by the bus	is the same as	the distance traveled by the truck.
$60t$	=	$45(t + 1.5)$

Solve
$$60t = 45(t + 1.5)$$
$$60t = 45t + 67.5 \qquad \text{Distribute the multiplication by 45: } 45(1.5) = 67.5.$$
$$15t = 67.5 \qquad \text{Subtract 45t from both sides: } 60t - 45t = 15t.$$
$$t = 4.5 \qquad \text{To isolate } t, \text{ divide both sides by 15: } \frac{67.5}{15} = 4.5.$$

State   The bus will overtake the truck in 4.5 or $4\frac{1}{2}$ hours.

Check   In 4.5 hours, the bus travels $60(4.5) = 270$ miles. The truck travels for $1.5 + 4.5 = 6$ hours at 45 mph, which is $45(6) = 270$ miles. Since the distance traveled are the same, the answer checks.

Success Tip   We used 1.5 hrs for the head start because it is easier to solve $60t = 45(t + 1.5)$ than $60t = 45\left(t + 1\frac{1}{2}\right)$.

Self Check 3
A car leaves a vacation spot traveling at 50 mph. Half an hour later, their friends leave the same spot in a second car traveling at 60 mph. How long will it take the second car to catch up with their friends?

Now Try **Problem 33**

3 Solve liquid mixture problems.

We now discuss how to solve mixture problems. In the first type, a liquid mixture of a desired strength is made from two solutions with different concentrations.

Self Check 4

How many gallons of a 3% salt solution must be mixed with a 7% salt solution to obtain 25 gallons of a 5.4% salt solution?

Now Try **Problem 43**

EXAMPLE 4   *Mixing Solutions*   A chemistry experiment calls for a 30% sulfuric acid solution. If the lab supply room has only 50% and 20% sulfuric acid solutions, how much of each should be mixed to obtain 12 liters of a 30% acid solution?

Analyze The 50% solution is too strong and the 20% solution is too weak. We must find how much of each should be combined to obtain 12 liters of a 30% solution.

Assign If x = the number of liters of the 50% solution used in the mixture, the remaining $(12 - x)$ liters must be the 20% solution. The amount of pure sulfuric acid in each solution is given by

> Amount of solution · strength of the solution = amount of pure sulfuric acid

A table and sketch are helpful in organizing the facts of the problem.

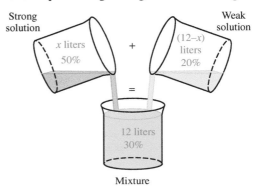

Mixture

	Amount ·	Strength =	**Amount of pure** **sulfuric acid**
Strong	x	0.50	$0.50x$
Weak	$12 - x$	0.20	$0.20(12 - x)$
Mixture	12	0.30	$12(0.30)$

Multiply amount · strength three times to fill in this column.

Enter this information first.

Use the information in this column to form an equation.

Form

The sulfuric acid in the 50% solution	plus	the sulfuric acid in the 20% solution	equals	the sulfuric acid in the mixture.
$0.50x$	$+$	$0.20(12 - x)$	$=$	$12(0.30)$

Solve

$$0.50x + 0.20(12 - x) = 12(0.30)$$

$$0.5x + 2.4 - 0.2x = 3.6 \qquad \text{Distribute the multiplication by 0.20.}$$

$$0.3x + 2.4 = 3.6 \qquad \text{Combine like terms: } 0.5x - 0.2x = 0.3x.$$

$$0.3x = 1.2 \qquad \text{Subtract 2.4 from both sides.}$$

$$x = 4 \qquad \text{To isolate } x, \text{ undo the multiplication by 0.3 by}$$
$$\text{dividing both sides by 0.3: } \frac{1.2}{0.3} = 4.$$

State 4 liters of 50% solution and $12 - 4 = 8$ liters of 20% solution should be used.

Check The amount of acid in 4 liters of the 50% solution is $0.50(4) = 2.0$ liters and the amount of acid in 8 liters of the 20% solution is $0.20(8) = 1.6$ liters. Thus, the amount of acid in these two solutions is $2.0 + 1.6 = 3.6$ liters. The amount of acid in 12 liters of the 30% mixture is also $0.30(12) = 3.6$ liters. Since the amounts of acid are equal, the answers check.

> **Success Tip** The strength *(concentration)* of a mixture is always between the strengths of the two solutions used to make it.

4 Solve dry mixture problems.

In another type of mixture problem, a dry mixture of a specified value is created from two differently priced ingredients.

EXAMPLE 5 *Snack Foods* Because cashews priced at $9 per pound were not selling, a produce clerk decided to combine them with less expensive peanuts and sell the mixture for $7 per pound. How many pounds of peanuts, selling at $6 per pound, should be mixed with 50 pounds of cashews to obtain such a mixture?

Analyze We need to determine how many pounds of peanuts to mix with 50 pounds of cashews to obtain a mixture worth $7 per pound.

Assign Let $x =$ the number of pounds of peanuts to use in the mixture. Since 50 pounds of cashews will be combined with the peanuts, the mixture will weigh $50 + x$ pounds. The value of the mixture and of each of its ingredients is given by

$$\text{Amount} \cdot \text{the price} = \text{the total value}$$

We can organize the facts of the problem in a table.

	Amount ·	Price =	Total value
Peanuts	x	6	$6x$
Cashews	50	9	450
Mixture	$50 + x$	7	$7(50 + x)$

Multiply amount · price three times to fill in this column.

Enter this information first.

Use the information in this column to form an equation.

Form

The value of the peanuts	plus	the value of the cashews	equals	the value of the mixture.
$6x$	$+$	450	$=$	$7(50 + x)$

Solve

$6x + 450 = 7(50 + x)$

$6x + 450 = 350 + 7x$ Distribute the multiplication by 7.

$450 = 350 + x$ To eliminate the term 6x on the left side, subtract 6x from both sides: $7x - 6x = x$.

$100 = x$ To isolate x, subtract 350 from both sides.

State 100 pounds of peanuts should be used in the mixture.

Self Check 5
Candy worth $1.90 per pound is to be mixed with 60 lb of a second candy selling for $1.20 per pound. How many pounds of the $1.90 per pound mixture should be used to make a mixture worth $1.48 per pound?

Now Try **Problem 53**

Check The value of 100 pounds of peanuts, at $6 per pound, is $100(6) = \$600$ and the value of 50 pounds of cashews, at $9 per pound, $50(9) = \$450$. Thus, the value of these two amounts is $1,050. Since the value of 150 pounds of the mixture, at $7 per pound, is also $150(7) = \$1,050$, the answer checks.

5 Solve number-value problems.

When problems deal with collections of different items having different values, we must distinguish between the *number of* and the *value of* the items. For these problems, we will use the fact that

$$\text{Number} \cdot \text{value} = \text{total value}$$

Self Check 6

A small electronics store sells iPods for $189, iPod skins for $32, and iTunes cards for $15. If they place an order for three times as many iPods as skins and 6 times as many iTunes cards as skins, how many of each did they order if the total before shipping and tax totaled $2,756?

Now Try **Problem 63**

EXAMPLE 6 *Dining Area Improvements* A restaurant owner needs to purchase some tables, chairs, and dinner plates for the dining area of her establishment. She plans to buy four chairs and four plates for each new table. She also plans to buy 20 additional plates in case of breakage. If a table costs $100, a chair $50, and a plate $5, how many of each can she buy if she takes out a loan for $6,500 to pay for the new items?

Analyze We know the *value* of each item: Tables cost $100, chairs cost $50, and plates cost $5 each. We need to find the *number* of tables, chairs, and plates she can purchase for $6,500.

Assign The number of chairs and plates she needs depends on the number of tables she buys. So we let t = the number of tables to be purchased. Since every table requires four chairs and four plates, she needs to order $4t$ chairs. Because 20 additional plates are needed, she should order $(4t + 20)$ plates. We can organize the facts of the problem in a table.

	Number ·	Value =	Total value
Tables	t	100	$100t$
Chairs	$4t$	50	$50(4t)$
Plates	$4t + 20$	5	$5(4t + 20)$
			Total: 6,500

Multiply number · value three times to fill in this column.

Enter this information first.

Use the information in this column to form an equation.

Form

The value of the tables	plus	the value of the chairs	plus	the value of the plates	equals	the value of the purchase.
$100t$	$+$	$50(4t)$	$+$	$5(4t + 20)$	$=$	6,500

Solve

$$100t + 50(4t) + 5(4t + 20) = 6,500$$
$$100t + 200t + 20t + 100 = 6,500 \quad \text{Do the multiplications and distribute.}$$
$$320t + 100 = 6,500 \quad \text{Combine like terms:}$$
$$\text{100t + 200t + 20t = 320t.}$$
$$320t = 6,400 \quad \text{Subtract 100 from both sides.}$$
$$t = 20 \quad \text{To isolate } t, \text{ divide both sides by 320.}$$

To find the number of chairs and plates to buy, we evaluate $4t$ and $4t + 20$ for $t = 20$.

Chairs: $4t = 4(20)$ *Plates:* $4t + 20 = 4(20) + 20$ Substitute 20 for t.
$\quad\quad\quad = 80$ $\quad\quad\quad\quad\quad\quad = 100$

State The owner needs to buy 20 tables, 80 chairs, and 100 plates.

Check The total value of 20 tables is $20(\$100) = \$2,000$, the total value of 80 chairs is $80(\$50) = \$4,000$, and the total value of 100 plates is $100(\$5) = \$500$. Because the total purchase is $\$2,000 + \$4,000 + \$500 = \$6,500$, the answers check.

ANSWERS TO SELF CHECKS

1. $2,400 at 2%, $1,800 at 3%   **2.** 3.5 hr   **3.** 2.5 hr   **4.** 10 gal   **5.** 40 lb
6. 12 iPods, 4 skins, 24 cards

SECTION 4.7 STUDY SET

VOCABULARY

Fill in the blanks.

1. Problems that involve depositing money are called _____ problems, and problems that involve moving vehicles are called uniform _____ problems.

2. Problems that involve combining ingredients are called _____ problems, and problems that involve collections of different items having different values are called _____ problems.

CONCEPTS

3. Complete the *principal column* given that part of $30,000 is invested in stocks and the rest in art.

	$P \cdot r \cdot t = I$			
Stocks	x			
Art	?			

4. A man made two investments that earned a combined annual interest of $280. Complete the table and then form an equation for this investment problem.

	P	$\cdot$	r	$\cdot t =$	I
Bank	x		0.04	1	
Stocks	$6,000 - x$		0.06	1	
				Total:	

5. Complete the *rate column* given that the eastbound plane flew 150 mph slower than the westbound plane.

	$r \cdot t = d$		
West	r		
East	?		

6. a. Complete the *time column* given that a runner wants to overtake a walker and the walker had a $\frac{1}{2}$-hour head start.

	$r \cdot t = d$		
Runner		t	
Walker		?	

b. Complete the *time column* given that part of a 6-hour drive was in fog and the other part was in clear conditions.

	$r \cdot t = d$		
Foggy		t	
Clear		?	

7. A husband and wife drive in opposite directions to work. Their drives last the same amount of time and their workplaces are 80 miles apart. Complete the table and then form an equation for this distance problem.

	$r \cdot t = d$		
Husband	35	t	
Wife	45		
		Total:	

8. a. How many gallons of acetic acid are there in barrel 2? (See the figure on the next page.)

b. Suppose the contents of the two barrels are poured into an empty third barrel. How many gallons of liquid will the third barrel contain?

c. Estimate the strength of the solution in the third barrel: 15%, 35%, or 60% acid?

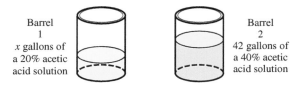

Barrel 1
x gallons of a 20% acetic acid solution

Barrel 2
42 gallons of a 40% acetic acid solution

9. a. Two antifreeze solutions are combined to form a mixture. Complete the table and then form an equation for this mixture problem.

	Amount	· Strength	= Pure antifreeze
Strong	6	0.50	
Weak	x	0.25	
Mixture		0.30	

b. Two oil-and-vinegar salad dressings are combined to make a new mixture. Complete the table and then form an equation for this mixture problem.

	Amount	· Strength	= Pure vinegar
Strong	x	0.06	
Weak		0.03	
Mixture	10	0.05	

10. The value of all the nylon brushes that a paint store carries is $670. Complete the table and then form an equation for this number-value problem.

	Number	· Value	= Total value
1-inch	$2x$	4	
2-inch	x	5	
3-inch	$x + 10$	7	
		Total:	

NOTATION

11. Write 6% and 15.2% in decimal form.

12. By what power of 10 should each decimal be multiplied to make it a whole number?
  a. 0.08   **b.** 0.162

GUIDED PRACTICE

Solve each equation. See Example 1.

13. $0.18x + 0.45(12 - x) = 0.36(12)$

14. $0.12x + 0.20(4 - x) = 0.6$

15. $0.08x + 0.07(15,000 - x) = 1,110$

16. $0.108x + 0.07(16,000 - x) = 1,500$

APPLICATIONS

Investment problems. See Example 1.

17. CORPORATE INVESTMENTS The financial board of a corporation invested $25,000 overseas, part at 4% and part at 7% annual interest. Find the amount invested at each rate if the first-year combined income from the two investments was $1,300.

18. LOANS A credit union loaned out $50,000, part at an annual rate of 5% and the rest at an annual rate of 8%. They collected combined simple interest of $3,400 from the loans that year. How much was loaned out at each rate?

19. OLD COINS A salesperson used her $3,500 year-end bonus to purchase some old coins, with hopes of earning 15% annual interest on the gold coins and 12% annual interest on the silver coins. If she saw return on her investment of $480 the first year, how much did she invest in each type of coin?

20. HIGH-RISK COMPANIES An investment club used funds totaling $200,000 to invest in a bio-tech company and in an ethanol plant, with hopes of earning 11% and 14% annual interest, respectively. Their hunch paid off. The club made a total of $24,250 interest the first year. How much was invested at each rate?

21. RETIREMENT A professor wants to supplement her pension with investment interest. If she invests $28,000 at 6% interest, how much would she have to invest at 7% to achieve a goal of $3,500 per year in supplemental income?

22. EXTRA INCOME An investor wants to receive $1,000 annually from two investments. He has put $4,500 in a money market account paying 4% annual interest. How much should he invest in a stock fund that pays 10% annual interest to achieve his goal?

23. 1099 FORMS The form on the next page shows the interest income Terrell Washington earned in 2012 from two savings accounts. He deposited a total of $15,000 at the first of that year, and made no further deposits or withdrawals. How much money did he deposit in account 822 and in account 721?

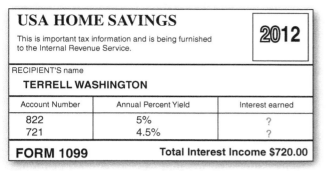

USA HOME SAVINGS

This is important tax information and is being furnished to the Internal Revenue Service.

2012

RECIPIENT'S name

TERRELL WASHINGTON

Account Number	Annual Percent Yield	Interest earned
822	5%	?
721	4.5%	?

FORM 1099   Total Interest Income $720.00

24. INVESTMENT PLANS A financial planner recommends a plan for a client who has $65,000 to invest. (See the chart.) At the end of the presentation, the client asks, "How much will be invested at each rate?" Answer this question using the given information.

Investment Plan

$65,000
to invest

Mutual fund
12%
annual rate

Municipal bonds
6.2%
annual rate

Total interest
$6,477.60
earned 1st year

25. INVESTMENTS Equal amounts are invested in each of three accounts paying 7%, 8%, and 10.5% annually. If one year's combined interest income is $1,249.50, how much is invested in each account?

26. PERSONAL LOANS Maggy lent her brother some money at 2% annual interest. She lent her sister twice as much money at half of the interest rate. In one year, Maggy collected combined interest of $200 from her brother and sister. How much did she lend each of them?

27. TAX RETURNS On a federal income tax form, Schedule B, a taxpayer forgot to write in the amount of interest income he earned for the year. From what is written on the form, determine the amount of interest earned from each investment and the amount he invested in stocks.

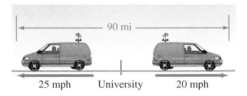

Schedule B–Interest and Dividend Income

Part 1
Interest
Income

Note: If you had over $400 in taxable income, use this form.

1 List name of payer.

(See pages 12 and B1.)

① MONEY MARKET ACCT.
DEPOSITED $15,000 @ 3.3%

② STOCKS
EARNED 5%

Amount

SAME
AMOUNT
FROM
EACH

28. MONEY-LAUNDERING Use the evidence compiled by investigators to determine how much money a suspect deposited in the Cayman Islands bank.

- On 6/1/11, the suspect electronically transferred $300,000 to a Swiss bank account paying an 8% annual yield.
- That same day, the suspect opened another account in a Cayman Islands bank that offered a 5% annual yield.
- A document dated 6/3/12 was seized during a raid of the suspect's home. It stated, "The total interest earned in one year from the two overseas accounts was 7.25% of the total amount deposited."

Uniform motion problems. See Examples 2–3.

29. TORNADOES During a storm, two teams of scientists leave a university at the same time in vans to search for tornadoes. The first team travels east at 20 mph and the second travels west at 25 mph. If their radios have a range of up to 90 miles, how long will it be before they lose radio contact?

90 mi

25 mph   University   20 mph

30. UNMANNED AIRCRAFT Two remotely controlled unmanned aircraft are launched in opposite directions. One flies east at 78 mph and the other west at 82 mph. How long will it take the aircraft to fly a combined distance of 560 miles?

31. HELLO/GOODBYE A husband and wife work different shifts at the same plant. When the husband leaves from work to make the 20-mile trip home, the wife leaves their home and drives to work. They travel on the same road. The husband's driving rate is 45 mph and the wife's is 35 mph. How long into their drives can they wave at each other when passing on the road?

32. AIR TRAFFIC CONTROL An airliner leaves Berlin, Germany, headed for Montreal, Canada, flying at an average speed of 450 mph. At the same time, an airliner leaves Montreal headed for Berlin, averaging 500 mph. If the airports are 3,800 miles apart, when will the air traffic controllers have to make the pilots aware that the planes are passing each other?

33. CYCLING A cyclist leaves his training base for a morning workout, riding at the rate of 18 mph. One and one-half hours later, his support staff leaves the base in a car going 45 mph in the same direction. How long will it take the support staff to catch up with the cyclist?

34. PARENTING How long will it take a mother, running at 4 feet per second, to catch up with her toddler, running down the sidewalk at 2 feet per second, if the child had a 5-second head start?

35. ROAD TRIPS A car averaged 40 mph for part of a trip and 50 mph for the remainder. If the 5-hour trip covered 210 miles, for how long did the car average 40 mph?

36. CROSS-TRAINING An athlete runs up a set of stadium stairs at a rate of 2 stairs per second, immediately turns around, and then descends the same stairs at a rate of 3 stairs per second. If the workout takes 90 seconds, how long does it take him to run up the stairs?

37. WINTER DRIVING A trucker drove for 4 hours before he encountered icy road conditions. He reduced his speed by 20 mph and continued driving for 3 more hours. Find his average speed during the first part of the trip if the entire trip was 325 miles.

38. SPEED OF TRAINS Two trains are 330 miles apart, and their speeds differ by 20 mph. Find the speed of each train if they are traveling toward each other and will meet in 3 hours.

39. PHYSICAL FITNESS For her workout, Sarah walks north at the rate of 3 mph and returns at the rate of 4 mph. How many miles does she walk if the round trip takes 3.5 hours?

40. PAPARAZZI A celebrity leaves a nightclub in his car and travels at 1 mile per minute (60 mph) trying to avoid a tabloid photographer. One minute later, the photographer leaves the nightclub on his motorcycle, traveling at 1.5 miles per minute (90 mph) in pursuit of the celebrity. How long will it take the photographer to catch up with the celebrity?

Liquid mixture problems. See Example 4.

41. SALT SOLUTIONS How many gallons of a 3% salt solution must be mixed with 50 gallons of a 7% solution to obtain a 5% solution?

42. PHOTOGRAPHY A photographer wishes to mix 2 liters of a 5% acetic acid solution with a 10% solution to get a 7% solution. How many liters of 10% solution must be added?

43. MAKING CHEESE To make low-fat cottage cheese, milk containing 4% butterfat is mixed with milk containing 1% butterfat to obtain 15 gallons of a mixture containing 2% butterfat. How many gallons of each milk must be used?

44. ANTIFREEZE How many quarts of a 10% antifreeze solution must be mixed with 16 quarts of a 40% antifreeze solution to make a 30% solution?

45. PRINTING A printer has ink that is 8% cobalt blue color and ink that is 22% cobalt blue color. How many ounces of each ink are needed to make 1 gallon (64 ounces) of ink that is 15% cobalt blue color?

46. FLOOD DAMAGE One website recommends a 6% chlorine bleach–water solution to remove mildew. A chemical lab has 3% and 15% chlorine bleach–water solutions in stock. How many gallons of each should be mixed to obtain 100 gallons of the mildew spray?

47. INTERIOR DECORATING The colors on the paint chip card below are created by adding different amounts of orange tint to a white latex base. How many gallons of Desert Sunrise should be mixed with 1 gallon of Bright Pumpkin to obtain Cool Cantaloupe?

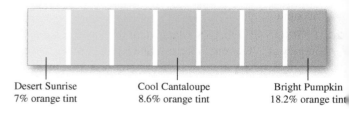

Desert Sunrise
7% orange tint

Cool Cantaloupe
8.6% orange tint

Bright Pumpkin
18.2% orange tint

48. ANTISEPTICS A nurse wants to add water to 30 ounces of a 10% solution of benzalkonium chloride to dilute it to an 8% solution. How much water must she add? (*Hint:* Water is 0% benzalkonium chloride.)

49.

from **Campus to Careers**

Registered Dietitian

Suppose, as registered dietitian for a school district, you must make sure that only extra lean ground beef (16% fat) is served in the cafeteria. Further suppose that the kitchen has 8 pounds of regular ground beef (30% fat) on hand. How many pounds of extra lean ground beef (12% fat) must be purchased and added to the regular ground beef to obtain a mixture that has the correct fat content?

50. INSECT REPELLANT The active ingredient used in most insect repellents is known as DEET (N-Diethyl-meta-toluamide). How many ounces of a 1.25% DEET solution and how many ounces of a 5% DEET solution should be mixed to produce 10 ounces of a 2.5% DEET solution? (*Hint:* Express the results as mixed numbers.)

51. DILUTING SOLUTIONS How much water should be added to 20 ounces of a 15% solution of alcohol to dilute it to a 10% alcohol solution?

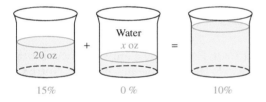

52. EVAPORATION The beaker shown below contains a 2% saltwater solution.

  a. How much water must be boiled away to increase the concentration of the salt solution from 2% to 3%?

  b. Where on the beaker would the new water level be? (mL means milliliter.)

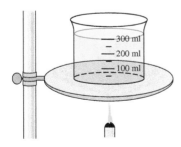

Dry mixture problems

53. LAWN SEED A store sells bluegrass seed for $6 per pound and ryegrass seed for $3 per pound. How much ryegrass must be mixed with 100 pounds of bluegrass to obtain a blend that will sell for $5 per pound?

54. COFFEE BLENDS A store sells regular coffee for $8 a pound and gourmet coffee for $14 a pound. To get rid of 40 pounds of the gourmet coffee, a shopkeeper makes a blend to put on sale for $10 a pound. How many pounds of regular coffee should he use?

55. RAISINS How many scoops of natural seedless raisins costing $3.45 per scoop must be mixed with 20 scoops of golden seedless raisins costing $2.55 per scoop to obtain a mixture costing $3 per scoop?

56. FERTILIZER Fertilizer with weed control costing $38 per 50-pound bag is to be mixed with a less expensive fertilizer costing $6 per 50-pound bag to make 16 bags of fertilizer that can be sold for $28 per bag. How many bags of cheaper fertilizer should be used?

57. PACKAGED SALAD How many 10-ounce bags of Romaine lettuce must be mixed with fifty 10-ounce bags of Iceberg lettuce to obtain a blend that sells for $2.50 per ten-ounce bag?

58. MIXING CANDY Lemon drops worth $3.80 per pound are to be mixed with jelly beans that cost $2.40 per pound to make 100 pounds of a mixture worth $2.96 per pound. How many pounds of each candy should be used?

59. BRONZE A pound of tin is worth $1 more than a pound of copper. Four pounds of tin are mixed with 6 pounds of copper to make bronze that sells for $3.65 per pound. How much is a pound of tin worth?

60. SNACK FOODS A bag of peanuts is worth $.30 less than a bag of cashews. Equal amounts of peanuts and cashews are used to make 40 bags of a mixture that sells for $1.05 per bag. How much is a bag of cashews worth?

61. METALLURGY A 1-ounce commemorative coin is to be made of a combination of pure gold, costing $380 an ounce, and a gold alloy that costs $140 an ounce. If the cost of the coin is to be $200, and 500 are to be minted, how many ounces of gold and gold alloy are needed to make the coins?

62. GARDENING A wholesaler of premium organic planting mix notices that the retail garden centers are not buying her product because of its high price of $1.57 per cubic foot. She decides to mix sawdust with the planting mix to lower the price per cubic foot. If the wholesaler can buy the sawdust for $0.10 per cubic foot, how many cubic feet of each must be mixed to have 6,000 cubic feet of planting mix that could be sold to retailers for $1.08 per cubic foot?

Number-value problems. See Example 6.

63. RENTALS The owners of an apartment building rent equal numbers of 1-, 2-, and 3-bedroom units. The monthly rent for a 1-bedroom is $550, a 2-bedroom is $700, and a 3-bedroom is $900. If the total monthly income is $36,550, how many of each type of unit are there?

64. WAREHOUSING A store warehouses 40 more portables than big-screen TV sets, and 15 more consoles than big-screen sets. The monthly storage cost for a portable is $1.50, a console is $4.00, and a big-screen is $7.50. If storage for all the televisions costs $276 per month, how many big-screen sets are in stock?

65. SOFTWARE Three software applications are priced as shown. Spreadsheet and database programs sold in equal numbers, but 15 more word processing applications were sold than the other two combined. If the three applications generated sales of $72,000, how many spreadsheets were sold?

Software	Price
Spreadsheet	$150
Database	$195
Word processing	$210

66. INVENTORIES With summer approaching, the number of air conditioners sold is expected to be double that of stoves and refrigerators combined. Stoves sell for $350, refrigerators for $450, and air conditioners for $500, and sales of $56,000 are expected. If stoves and refrigerators sell in equal numbers, how many of each appliance should be stocked?

67. PIGGY BANKS When a child emptied his coin bank, he had a collection of pennies, nickels, and dimes. There were 20 more pennies than dimes and the number of nickels was triple the number of dimes. If the coins had a value of $5.40, how many of each type coin were in the bank?

68. WISHING WELLS A scuba diver, hired by an amusement park, collected $121 in nickels, dimes, and quarters at the bottom of a wishing well. There were 500 nickels, and 90 more quarters than dimes. How many quarters and dimes were thrown into the wishing well?

69. BASKETBALL Epiphanny Prince, of New York, scores 113 points in a high school game on February 1, 2006, breaking a national prep record that was held by Cheryl Miller. Prince made 46 more 2-point baskets than 3-point baskets, and only 1 free throw. How many 2-point and 3-point baskets did she make?

70. MUSEUM TOURS The admission prices for the World of Coca-Cola Museum in Atlanta are shown. A family purchased 3 more children's tickets than adult tickets, and 1 less senior ticket than adult tickets. The total cost of the tickets was $148. How many of each type of ticket did they purchase?

ADMISSION PRICES
Adults $16
Seniors $14
Children . . . $12

71. HALL OF FAME The admission prices for the NASCAR Hall of Fame in Charlotte, North Carolina, are shown below. A family purchased 4 times as many adult tickets as children's tickets, 2 less senior tickets than adult tickets, and 1 military ticket. The total cost of the tickets was $138.60. How many of each type ticket did they purchase?

General Admission Ticket Prices	
Adults	$18.95
Seniors (60+)	$16.95
Military	$16.95
Children (5-12)	$11.95

72. SELLING CALCULATORS Last month, a bookstore ran the following ad. Sales of $5,370 were generated, with 15 more graphing calculators sold than scientific calculators. How many of each type of calculator did the bookstore sell?

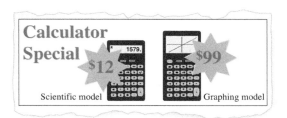

Calculator Special
$12 Scientific model $99 Graphing model

75. Write an investment problem to fit the following equation, and then solve it.

$$0.08x + 0.07(10{,}000 - x) = 770$$

76. Explain the error in each statement.

  a. If 3 pounds of Mocha coffee are mixed with x pounds of Java coffee, there will be $3x$ pounds of the Mocha-Java blend.

  b. A financial manager has a total of $5,000 to invest in two accounts. If $\$x$ is invested in the first account, then $\$(x - 5{,}000)$ is left to be invested in the second account.

WRITING

73. Create a mixture problem of your own, and solve it.

74. Is it possible to mix a 10% sugar solution with a 20% sugar solution to get a 30% sugar solution? Explain.

SECTION 4.8
Applications Introduction: Inequalities

We have seen that an **equation** is a statement indicating that two algebraic expressions are equal. Algebra, however, is not only about expressions that are equal. Sometimes we need to compare expressions that are not equal. Comparisons of that type can be made using an *inequality*. An **inequality** is a mathematical statement that contains one (or more) of the following symbols.

Inequality Symbols

$<$ is less than	$>$ is greater than	$\neq$ is not equal to
$\leq$ is less than or equal to	$\geq$ is greater than or equal to	

Here are some examples of inequalities:

- $1 < 5$ Read as "1 is less than 5." This is a true inequality because 1 lies to the left of 5 on a number line.

- $24 > -37$ Read as "24 is greater than -37." This is a true inequality because 24 lies to the right of -37 on a number line.

- $9 \leq 50$ Read as "9 is less than or equal to fifty." This is a true inequality because 9 is less than 50.

- $212 \leq 212$ Read as "212 is less than or equal to 212." This is a true inequality because 212 is equal to 212.

When we make comparisons of the relative sizes of numbers in our daily lives, we often do so using words. For example, a shopper might comment that the price of an item for sale on the Internet is *less than* its price at a local department store, or a student might claim that her college GPA is *greater than* her high school GPA. Those comparisons can be written in symbols using an inequality:

Internet price < department store price   college GPA > high school GPA

1. **VEHICLE SAFTEY** All motor vehicles registered in North Carolina that are less than 35 years old are required to pass a safety inspection.

   a. Which of the following vehicle ages must have the safety inspection?

      21 years old   9 years old   35 years old   14 years old   37 years old

   b. Which of the vehicle ages above do *not* need to have the safety inspection?

   c. Let a = the age (in years) of a registered vehicle. Fill in the blank with an inequality symbol to describe the age requirement for a safety inspection.

   a ▢ 35

2. **THE IRS** A federal income tax filer is disqualified from claiming an earned income credit if his or her investment income is more than $3,150.

   a. Which of the following interest incomes disqualify the tax filer to claim an earned income tax credit?

      $1,315 $ 3,151 $3,510 $3,150 $5,031 $ 3,149

   b. Which of the interest incomes listed above qualify a tax filer for an earned income tax credit?

   c. Let i = the interest income (in dollars) of a tax filer. Fill in the blank with an inequality symbol to describe the amount of interest income that disqualifies a filer from claiming an earned income tax credit.

   i ▢ 3,150

3. **ROLLER COASTERS** The sign shown below applies to the *Intimidator* roller coaster at the Carowinds amusement park on the state line between North Carolina and South Carolina. The symbol " stands for inches.

   a. Which of the following heights satisfy the requirement printed on the sign?

      56"   53"   54"   61"   47"   50"

   b. Which of the heights listed above do *not* satisfy the requirement printed on the sign?

   c. Let h = the height (in inches) of a person. Fill in the blank with an inequality symbol to describe the height requirement printed on the sign.

   h ▢ 54

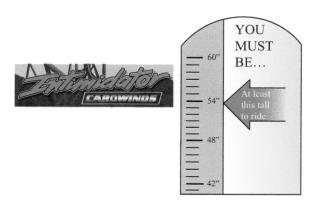

4. OCCUPANCY The sign shown below was posted in a college cafeteria.

  a. Which of the following numbers of persons satisfy the requirement printed on the sign?

  108 persons   190 persons   167 persons   181 persons   99 persons   180 persons

  b. Which of the numbers of persons listed above do *not* satisfy the requirement printed on the sign?

  c. Let the variable m = the maximum occupancy of the cafeteria. Fill in the blank with an inequality symbol to describe the occupancy requirement printed on the sign.

$$m \quad 180$$

MAXIMUM
OCCUPANCY
NOT TO EXCEED

180 PERSONS

In problems 5-10, let a variable represent the unknown quantity. Then write an inequality to describe the situation. The first problem is done for you. Answers may vary depending on the variable chosen.

5. SOCIAL MEDIA *Twitter* is an online social networking service that enables its users to send and read text-based posts of up to 140 characters.

  Let c = the number of characters in a text message $c \leq 140$

6. PASSWORDS Many banks require customer online account passwords to be at least 8 characters long.

7. TRAVELING WITH PETS *American Airlines* accepts small cats and dogs in the cabin of the aircraft on both domestic and international flights. The combined weight of the pet and carrier may not surpass 20 pounds.

8. TUITION COSTS North Carolina legislation states that a student enrolling in the same occupational extension course more than twice within a five-year period shall pay their cost for the course

9. PREGNANCY One medical website recommends that women go to the hospital when their contractions are less than 5 minutes apart,

10. SWINGS The instructions for building a tree rope swing suggests the horizontal tree branch to be used should be at most 12 feet off the ground.

Objectives

1 Determine whether a number is a solution of an inequality.

2 Graph solution sets and use interval notation.

3 Solve linear inequalities.

4 Solve compound inequalities.

5 Solve inequality applications.

SECTION 4.8

Solving Inequalities

ARE YOU READY?

The following problems review some basic skills that are needed to solve inequalities.

1. Fill in the blanks: The symbol $<$ means " ___ ___ ___."

2. Is $-5 > -6$ a true or false statement?

3. Graph each number in the set $\left\{ -4, -1.7, 2, \dfrac{13}{4} \right\}$ on a number line.

4. Express the fact that $10 > 0$ using an $<$ symbol.

In our daily lives, we often speak of one value being *greater than* or *less than* another. For example, a sick child might have a temperature *greater than* 98.6°F or a granola bar might contain *less than* 2 grams of fat.

In mathematics, we use *inequalities* to show that one expression is greater than or is less than another expression.

1 **Determine whether a number is a solution of an inequality.**

An **inequality** is a statement that contains one or more of the following symbols.

Inequality Symbols		
$<$ is less than	$>$ is greater than	$\neq$ is not equal to
$\leq$ is less than or equal to	$\geq$ is greater than or equal to	

An inequality can be true, false, or neither true nor false. For example,

- $9 \geq 9$ is true because $9 = 9$.
- $37 < 24$ is false.
- $x + 1 > 5$ is neither true nor false because we don't know what number x represents.

An inequality that contains a variable can be made true or false depending on the number that is substituted for the variable. If we substitute 10 for x in $x + 1 > 5$, the resulting inequality is true: $10 + 1 > 5$. If we substitute 1 for x, the resulting inequality is false: $1 + 1 > 5$. A number that makes an inequality true is called a **solution** of the inequality, and we say that the number *satisfies* the inequality. Thus, 10 is a solution of $x + 1 > 5$ and 1 is not.

> **The Language of Algebra** Because $<$ requires one number to be strictly less than another number and $>$ requires one number to be strictly greater than another number, $<$ and $>$ are called *strict inequalities*.

In this section, we will find the solutions of *linear inequalities in one variable.*

Linear Inequality in One Variable

A **linear inequality in one variable** can be written in one of the following forms where a, b, and c are real numbers and $a \neq 0$.

$$ax + b > c \qquad ax + b \geq c \qquad ax + b < c \qquad ax + b \leq c$$

EXAMPLE 1   Is 9 a solution of $2x + 4 \leq 21$?

Strategy We will substitute 9 for x and evaluate the expression on the left side.

WHY If a true statement results, 9 is a solution of the inequality. If we obtain a false statement, 9 is not a solution.

Solution

$$2x + 4 \leq 21$$
$$2(9) + 4 \overset{?}{\leq} 21 \qquad \text{Substitute 9 for x. Read } \overset{?}{\leq} \text{ as "is possibly less than or equal to."}$$
$$18 + 4 \overset{?}{\leq} 21$$
$$22 \leq 21 \qquad \text{This inequality is false.}$$

The statement $22 \leq 21$ is false because neither $22 < 21$ nor $22 = 21$ is true. Therefore, 9 is not a solution.

Self Check 1

Is 2 a solution of $3x - 1 \geq 0$?

Now Try **Problem 13**

2 Graph solution sets and use interval notation.

The **solution set** of an inequality is the set of all numbers that make the inequality true. Some solution sets are easy to determine. For example, if we replace the variable in $x > -3$ with a number greater than -3, the resulting inequality will be true. Because there are infinitely many real numbers greater than -3, it follows that $x > -3$ has infinitely many solutions. Since there are too many solutions to list, we use **set-builder notation** to describe the solutions set.

$$\{x \mid x > -3\} \qquad \text{Read as "the set of all x such that x is greater than } -3."$$

We can illustrate the solution set by **graphing the inequality** on a number line. To graph $x > -3$, a **parenthesis** or **open circle** is drawn on the endpoint -3 to indicate that -3 is not part of the graph. Then we shade all of the points on the number line to the right of -3. The right arrowhead is also shaded to show that the solutions continue forever to the right.

Method 1: parenthesis   Method 2: open circle

All real numbers greater than -3

The graph of $x > -3$ is an example of an **interval** on the number line. We can write intervals in a compact form called **interval notation.**

The interval notation that represents the graph of $x > -3$ is $(-3, \infty)$. As on the number line, a left parenthesis is written next to -3 to indicate that -3 is not included in the interval. The **positive infinity symbol** ∞ that follows indicates that the interval continues without end to the right. With this notation, *a parenthesis is always used next to an infinity symbol.*

The illustration below shows the relationship between the symbols used to graph an interval and the corresponding interval notation. If we begin at -3 and move to the right, the shaded arrowhead on the graph indicates that the interval approaches positive infinity ∞.

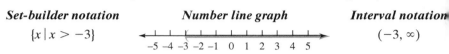

(-3, ∞)

We now have three ways to describe the solution set of an inequality.

Set-builder notation	*Number line graph*	*Interval notation*
{x	x > -3}	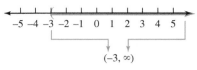	(-3, ∞)

> *Success Tip* The *infinity* symbol ∞ does not represent a number. It indicates that an interval extends to the right without end.

Self Check 2
Graph: $x \geq 0$

Now Try **Problem 17**

EXAMPLE 2   Graph: $x \leq 2$

Strategy We need to determine which real numbers, when substituted for x, would make $x \leq 2$ a true statement.

WHY To graph $x \leq 2$ means to draw a "picture" of all of the values of x that make the inequality true.

Solution
If we replace x with a number less than or equal to 2, the resulting inequality will be true. To graph the solution set, a **bracket** or a **closed circle** is drawn at the endpoint 2 to indicate that 2 is part of the graph. Then we shade all of the points on the number line to the left of 2 and the left arrowhead.

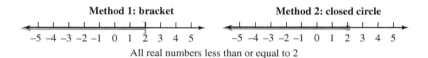

All real numbers less than or equal to 2

The interval is written as $(-\infty, 2]$. The right bracket indicates that 2 is included in the interval. The **negative infinity symbol** $-\infty$ shows that the interval continues forever to the left. The illustration below shows the relationship between the symbols used to graph the interval and the corresponding interval notation.

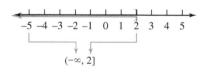

(-∞, 2]

3 Solve linear inequalities.

To **solve an inequality** means to find all values of the variable that make the inequality true. As with equations, there are properties that we can use to solve inequalities.

> ### Addition and Subtraction Properties of Inequality
>
> Adding the same number to, or subtracting the same number from, both sides of an inequality does not change its solutions.
>
> For any real numbers a, b, and c,
>
> > If $a < b$, then $a + c < b + c$.
> > If $a < b$, then $a - c < b - c$.
>
> Similar statements can be made for the symbols $\leq$, $>$, and $\geq$.

After applying one of these properties, the resulting inequality is equivalent to the original one. **Equivalent inequalities** have the same solution set.

Like equations, inequalities are solved by isolating the variable on one side.

EXAMPLE 3   Solve $x + 3 > 2$. Write the solution set in interval notation and graph it.

Strategy We will use a property of inequality to isolate the variable on one side.

WHY To solve the original inequality, we want to find a simpler equivalent inequality of the form $x > $ **a number** or $x < $ **a number**, whose solution is obvious.

Solution

We will use the subtraction property of inequality to isolate x on the left side of the inequality. We can undo the addition of 3 by subtracting 3 from both sides.

$$x + 3 > 2 \qquad \text{This is the inequality to solve.}$$
$$x + 3 - 3 > 2 - 3 \qquad \text{Subtract 3 from both sides.}$$
$$x > -1$$

All real numbers greater than -1 are solutions of $x + 3 > 2$. The solution set can be written in set-builder notation as $\{x \mid x > -1\}$ and in interval notation as $(-1, \infty)$. The graph of the solution set is shown below.

$$\text{(number line graph from } -3 \text{ to } 3 \text{ with open parenthesis at } -1)$$

Since there are infinitely many solutions, we cannot check all of them.

As an informal check, we can pick some numbers in the graph, say 0 and 30, substitute each number for x in the original inequality, and see whether true statements result.

Check:
$$x + 3 > 2 \qquad\qquad\qquad x + 3 > 2$$
$$0 + 3 \stackrel{?}{>} 2 \quad \text{Substitute 0 for x.} \qquad 30 + 3 \stackrel{?}{>} 2 \quad \text{Substitute 30 for x.}$$
$$3 > 2 \quad \text{True} \qquad\qquad\qquad 33 > 2 \quad \text{True}$$

The solution set appears to be correct.

Caution! Since we use parentheses and brackets in interval notation, we will use them to graph inequalities. Note that parentheses, not brackets, are written next to ∞ and $-\infty$ because there is no endpoint.

$$(-3, \infty) \qquad (-\infty, 2]$$

As with equations, there are properties for multiplying and dividing both sides of an inequality by the same number. To develop what is called *the multiplication property of inequality,* we consider the true statement $2 < 5$. If both sides are multiplied by a positive number, such as 3, another true inequality results.

$$2 < 5 \qquad \text{This inequality is true.}$$
$$3 \cdot 2 < 3 \cdot 5 \qquad \text{Multiply both sides by 3.}$$
$$6 < 15 \qquad \text{This inequality is true.}$$

Self Check 3

Solve $x - 3 < -2$. Write the solution set in interval notation and graph it.

Now Try **Problem 25**

However, if we multiply both sides of $2 < 5$ by a negative number, such as -3, the direction of the inequality symbol is reversed to produce another true inequality.

$$2 < 5 \qquad \text{This inequality is true.}$$
$$-3 \cdot 2 > -3 \cdot 5 \qquad \text{Multiply both sides by } -3 \text{ and reverse the direction of the inequality.}$$
$$-6 > -15 \qquad \text{This inequality is true.}$$

The inequality $-6 > -15$ is true because -6 is to the right of -15 on the number line.

Dividing both sides of an inequality by the same negative number also requires that the direction of the inequality symbol be reversed.

$$-4 < 6 \qquad \text{This inequality is true.}$$
$$\frac{-4}{-2} > \frac{6}{-2} \qquad \text{Divide both sides by } -2 \text{ and change } < \text{ to } >.$$
$$2 > -3 \qquad \text{This inequality is true.}$$

These examples illustrate the multiplication and division properties of inequality.

Multiplication and Division Properties of Inequality

Multiplying or dividing both sides of an inequality by the same positive number does not change its solutions.

For any real numbers a, b, and c, where c is positive,

$$\text{If } a < b, \quad \text{then } ac < bc. \qquad \text{If } a < b, \quad \text{then } \frac{a}{c} < \frac{b}{c}.$$

If we multiply or divide both sides of an inequality by a negative number, the direction of the inequality symbol must be reversed for the inequalities to have the same solutions.

For any real numbers a, b, and c, where c is negative,

$$\text{If } a < b, \quad \text{then } ac > bc. \qquad \text{If } a < b, \text{ then } \frac{a}{c} > \frac{b}{c}.$$

Similar statements can be made for the symbols $\leq$, $>$, and $\geq$.

Self Check 4

Solve each inequality. Write the solution set in interval notation and graph it.

a. $-\frac{h}{20} \leq 10$

$\qquad -200 \quad 0 \quad 200$

b. $-12a > -144$

$\qquad 10 \quad 11 \quad 12 \quad 13$

EXAMPLE 4   Solve each inequality. Write the solution set in interval notation and graph it.   **a.** $-\frac{3}{2}t \geq -12$ **b.** $-5t < 55$

Strategy We will use a property of inequality to isolate the variable on one side.

WHY To solve the original inequality, we want to find a simpler equivalent inequality, whose solution is obvious.

Solution

a. To undo the multiplication by $-\frac{3}{2}$, we multiply both sides by the reciprocal, which is $-\frac{2}{3}$.

$$-\frac{3}{2}t \geq -12 \qquad \text{This is the inequality to solve.}$$

$$-\frac{2}{3}\left(-\frac{3}{2}t\right) \leq -\frac{2}{3}(-12) \qquad \begin{array}{l}\text{Multiply both sides by } -\frac{2}{3}. \text{ Since we are multiplying} \\ \text{both sides by a negative number, reverse the direction} \\ \text{of the inequality.}\end{array}$$

$$t \leq 8 \qquad \text{Do the multiplications.}$$

The solution set is $(-\infty, 8]$ and it is graphed as shown.

Now Try **Problems 31 and 33**

b. To undo the multiplication by -5, we divide both sides by -5.

$$-5t < 55$$ This is the inequality to solve.

$$\frac{-5t}{-5} > \frac{55}{-5}$$ To isolate t, undo the multiplication by -5 by dividing both sides by -5. Since we are dividing both sides by a negative number, reverse the direction of the inequality.

$$t > -11$$

The solution set is $(-11, \infty)$ and it is graphed as shown.

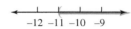

EXAMPLE 5 Solve $-5 > 3x + 7$. Write the solution set in interval notation and graph it.

Strategy First we will use a property of inequality to isolate the *variable term* on one side. Then we will use a second property of inequality to isolate the *variable* itself.

WHY To solve the original inequality, we want to find a simpler equivalent inequality of the form $x >$ **a number** or $x <$ **a number**, whose solution is obvious.

Solution

$$-5 > 3x + 7$$ This is the inequality to solve.

$$-5 - 7 > 3x + 7 - 7$$ To isolate the variable term, $3x$, undo the addition of 7 by subtracting 7 from both sides.

$$-12 > 3x$$ Do the subtractions.

$$\frac{-12}{3} > \frac{3x}{3}$$ To isolate x, undo the multiplication by 3 by dividing both sides by 3.

$$-4 > x$$ Do the divisions.

To determine the solution set, it is useful to rewrite the inequality $-4 > x$ in an equivalent form with the variable on the left side. If -4 is greater than x, it follows that x must be less than -4.

$$x < -4$$

The solution set is $(-\infty, -4)$, whose graph is shown below.

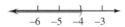

Self Check 5
Solve $-13 < 2r - 7$. Write the solution set in interval notation and graph it.

Now Try **Problem 39**

EXAMPLE 6 Solve $5.1 - 3k < 19.5$. Write the solution set in interval notation and graph it.

Strategy We will use properties of inequality to isolate the variable on one side.

WHY To solve the original inequality, we want to find a simpler equivalent inequality of the form $k >$ **a number** or $k <$ **a number**, whose solution is obvious.

Self Check 6
Solve $-9n + 1.8 > -17.1$. Write the solution set in interval notation and graph it.

Now Try **Problem 47**

Solution

$$5.1 - 3k < 19.5 \qquad \text{This is the inequality to solve.}$$

$$5.1 - 3k - \mathbf{5.1} < 19.5 - \mathbf{5.1} \qquad \text{To isolate } -3k \text{ on the left side, subtract 5.1 from both sides.}$$

$$-3k < 14.4 \qquad \text{Do the subtractions.}$$

$$\frac{-3k}{-3} > \frac{14.4}{-3} \qquad \text{To isolate } k, \text{ undo the multiplication by } -3 \text{ by dividing both sides by } -3 \text{ and reverse the direction of the } < \text{ symbol.}$$

$$k > -4.8 \qquad \text{Do the divisions.}$$

The solution set is $(-4.8, \infty)$, whose graph is shown below.

The equation solving strategy on page 163 can be applied to inequalities. However, when solving inequalities, we must remember to *change the direction of the inequality symbol when multiplying or dividing both sides by a negative number.*

Self Check 7

Solve $5(b - 2) \geq -(b - 3) + 2b$. Write the solution set in interval notation and graph it.

Now Try **Problem 53**

EXAMPLE 7   Solve $8(y + 1) \geq 2(y - 4) + y$. Write the solution set in interval notation and graph it.

Strategy We will follow the steps of the equation-solving strategy (adapted to inequalities) to solve the inequality.

WHY This is the most efficient way to solve a linear inequality in one variable.

Solution

$$8(y + 1) \geq 2(y - 4) + y \qquad \text{This is the inequality to solve.}$$

$$8y + 8 \geq 2y - 8 + y \qquad \text{Distribute the multiplication by 8 and by 2.}$$

$$8y + 8 \geq 3y - 8 \qquad \text{Combine like terms: } 2y + y = 3y.$$

$$8y + 8 - \mathbf{3y} \geq 3y - 8 - \mathbf{3y} \qquad \text{To eliminate 3y from the right side, subtract 3y from both sides.}$$

$$5y + 8 \geq -8 \qquad \text{Combine like terms on both sides.}$$

$$5y + 8 - \mathbf{8} \geq -8 - \mathbf{8} \qquad \text{To isolate 5y, undo the addition of 8 by subtracting 8 from both sides.}$$

$$5y \geq -16 \qquad \text{Do the subtractions.}$$

$$\frac{5y}{5} \geq \frac{-16}{5} \qquad \text{To isolate } y, \text{ undo the multiplication by 5 by dividing both sides by 5. Do not reverse the direction of the } \geq \text{ symbol.}$$

$$y \geq -\frac{16}{5}$$

The solution set is $\left[-\frac{16}{5}, \infty\right)$. To graph it, we note that $-\frac{16}{5} = -3\frac{1}{5}$.

4 Solve compound inequalities.

Two inequalities can be combined into a **compound inequality** to show that an expression lies between two fixed values. For example, $-2 < x < 3$ is a combination of

$$-2 < x \quad \text{and} \quad x < 3$$

It indicates that x is greater than -2 and that x is also less than 3. The solution set of $-2 < x < 3$ consists of all numbers that lie between -2 and 3, and we write it as $(-2, 3)$. The graph of the compound inequality is shown below.

EXAMPLE 8   Graph: $-4 \le x < 0$

Strategy We need to determine which real numbers, when substituted for x, would make $-4 \le x < 0$ a true statement.

WHY To graph $-4 \le x < 0$ means to draw a "picture" of all of the values of x that make the compound inequality true.

Solution

If we replace the variable in $-4 \le x < 0$ with a number between -4 and 0, including -4, the resulting compound inequality will be true. Therefore, the solution set is the interval $[-4, 0)$. To graph the interval, we draw a bracket at -4, a parenthesis at 0, and shade in between.

To check, we pick a number in the graph, such as -2, and see whether it satisfies the inequality. Since $-4 \le -2 < 0$ is true, the answer appears to be correct.

> **Success Tip**   Note that the two inequality symbols in $-4 \le x < 0$ point in the same direction and point to the smaller number.

To solve compound inequalities, we isolate the variable in the middle part of the inequality. To do this, we apply the properties of inequality to all *three* parts of the inequality.

EXAMPLE 9   Solve $-4 < 2(x - 1) \le 4$. Write the solution set in interval notation and graph it.

Strategy We will use properties of inequality to isolate the variable by itself as the middle part of the inequality.

WHY To solve the original inequality, we want to find a simpler equivalent inequality of the form a number $< x \le$ a number, whose solution is obvious.

Solution

$$-4 < 2(x - 1) \le 4 \qquad \text{This is the compound inequality to solve.}$$
$$-4 < 2x - 2 \le 4 \qquad \text{Distribute the multiplication by 2.}$$
$$-4 + 2 < 2x - 2 + 2 \le 4 + 2 \qquad \text{To isolate } 2x, \text{ undo the subtraction of 2 by adding 2 to all three parts.}$$

Self Check 8

Graph $-2 \le x < 1$ and write the solution set in interval notation.

Now Try **Problem 61**

Self Check 9

Solve $-6 \le 3(t + 2) \le 6$. Write the solution set in interval notation and graph it.

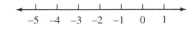

Now Try Problem 69

$$-2 < 2x \le 6 \qquad \text{Do the additions.}$$

$$\frac{-2}{2} < \frac{2x}{2} \le \frac{6}{2} \qquad \begin{array}{l}\text{To isolate x, we undo the multiplication by 2 by}\\ \text{dividing all three parts by 2.}\end{array}$$

$$-1 < x \le 3 \qquad \text{Do the divisions.}$$

The solution set is $(-1, 3]$ and its graph is shown.

> **Success Tip**   Think of interval notation as a way to tell someone how to draw the graph, from left to right, giving them only a "start" and a "stop" instruction.

5 Solve inequality applications.

In some application problems, an inequality, rather than an equation, is needed to find the solution. This is the case when we are asked to determine when one quantity *is more* (or *is less*) than another. Other phrases that call for an inequality are listed in the table below.

The statement	Translates to	The statement	Translates to
a does not exceed *b*.	$a \le b$	*a* will exceed *b*.	$a > b$
a is at most *b*.	$a \le b$	*a* surpasses *b*.	$a > b$
a is no more than *b*.	$a \le b$	*a* is at least *b*.	$a \ge b$
a is between b and c.	$b < a < c$	*a* is not less than *b*.	$a \ge b$

Self Check 10

CAR ENGINES   Refer to Example 7. Use an inequality to determine the rpm at which the output of a Porsche engine is no more than 240 horsepower.

Now Try Problem 93

EXAMPLE 10   *Car Engines*   The horsepower *h* produced by the engine in a Porsche 911 can be approximated by the formula $h = 0.06r - 36$, where r is the engine speed in revolutions per minute (rpm). Use an inequality to determine the rpm at which the output of the engine is at least 300 horsepower. (Source: ultimatecarpage.com)

Strategy Since *r* represents the rpm of the engine and *h* the horsepower it produces, we need to find the values of *r* for which $h \ge 300$.

WHY The phrase at least means to be greater than or equal to and, therefore, translates to the inequality symbol $\ge$.

Solution

$$h \ge 300 \qquad \text{We want the horsepower h to be greater than or equal to 300.}$$

$$0.06r - 36 \ge 300 \qquad \text{Substitute 0.06r} - 36 \text{ for h.}$$

$$0.06r \ge 336 \qquad \text{To isolate the variable term 0.06r, add 36 to both sides.}$$

$$\frac{0.06r}{0.06} \ge \frac{336}{0.06} \qquad \text{To isolate the variable r, divide both sides by 0.06.}$$

$$r \ge 5{,}600 \qquad \text{Do the division.}$$

The output of the engine exceeds 300 horsepower when the engine speed is 5,600 rpm or greater.

For more complicated application problems involving inequalities, we can adapt the six-step problem-solving strategy used in earlier chapters to find the solution. In such cases, Steps 3 and 4 of the strategy are as follows:

    3. Form an inequality by translating the words of the problem into mathematical symbols.

    4. Solve the inequality.

EXAMPLE 11   *Grades*   A student has scores of 72%, 74%, and 78% on three exams. What percent score does he need on the last exam to earn a grade of no less than B (80%)?

Analyze We know three scores. We are to find what the student must score on the last exam to earn a grade of B or higher.

Assign We can let x = the score on the fourth (and last) exam. To find the average grade, we add the four scores and divide by 4.

Form To earn a grade of *no less than* B, the student's average must be *greater than or equal to* 80%.

The average of the four grades	must be no less than	80.
$\dfrac{72 + 74 + 78 + x}{4}$	$\geq$	80

Solve

$$\frac{224 + x}{4} \geq 80 \qquad \text{Combine like terms in the numerator: } 72 + 74 + 78 = 224.$$

$$4\left(\frac{224 + x}{4}\right) \geq 4\,(80) \qquad \text{To clear the inequality of the fraction, multiply both sides by 4.}$$

$$224 + x \geq 320 \qquad \text{Simplify each side.}$$

$$x \geq 96 \qquad \text{To isolate x, undo the addition of 224 by subtracting 224 from both sides.}$$

State To earn a B, the student must score 96% or better on the last exam. Assuming the student cannot score higher than 100% on the exam, the solution set is written as [96, 100]. The graph is shown below.

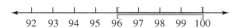

Check Pick some numbers in the interval, and verify that the average of the four scores will be 80% or greater.

Self Check 11

A student has scores of 78%, 82%, and 76% on three exams. What percent score does he need on the last test to earn a grade of no less than a B (80%)?

Now Try **Problem 111**

In the next example, an inequality is used to compare two rental plans to determine which one is financially better.

EXAMPLE 12   *Renting RVs*   *Adventure RVs* charges $2,300 and $0.28 per mile to rent a 36-foot recreational vehicle for one week. *Roadmaster RV's* weekly charge for the same model is $1,900 and $0.36 per mile. For what range of miles driven is *Adventure RV's* rental plan better?

Analyze *Adventure RV's* rental plan will be the better deal if it costs less than *Roadmaster RV's* rental plan. The phrase *less than* indicates an inequality should be used to model the situation.

Assign Let m = the number of miles the RV is driven during the week it is rented.

Form We can use the following formula to write algebraic expressions that represent the cost to rent the RV from each company:

The cost to rent the RV for a week	is	the basic fee	+	the cost per mile	·	the number of miles driven.

RENTING CARS *Great Value Car Rental* charges $12 a day and $0.15 per mile to rent a Ford Fusion. *Be Thrifty Car Rental's* daily charge for the same car is $15 and $0.12 per mile. If a businessman wants to rent the car for one day, for what range of miles driven is the *Be Thrifty* rental plan better?

Now Try **Problem 123**

Thus,

Adventure RV's cost = 2,300 + 0.28m   and   *Roadmaster RV's* cost = 1,900 + 0.36m

We want to find the range of miles that can be driven during the week so that:

The cost to rent the RV from *Adventure RVs*	is less than	the cost to rent the RV from *Roadmaster RVs.*
2,300 + 0.28m	<	1,900 + 0.36m

Solve

$$2,300 + 0.28m < 1,900 + 0.36m$$

$$2,300 < 1,900 + 0.08m \qquad \text{To eliminate } 0.28m \text{ on the left side, subtract } 0.28m \text{ from both sides: } 0.36m - 0.28m = 0.08m.$$

$$400 < 0.08m \qquad \text{To isolate the variable term } 0.08m \text{ on the right side, subtract 1,900 from both sides: } 2,300 - 1,900 = 400.$$

$$\frac{400}{0.08} < \frac{0.08m}{0.08} \qquad \text{To isolate } m \text{ on the right side, undo the multiplication by 0.08 by dividing both sides by 0.08.}$$

$$5,000 < m \qquad \text{Do the division.}$$

$$m > 5,000 \qquad \text{Write an equivalent inequality with the variable on the left side.}$$

State *Adventure RVs* will be the better deal if the RV is going to be driven more than 5,000 miles during the week.

Check We can check the result by calculating each RV rental for a number of miles driven that is slightly greater than 5,000, say 5,010.

Asventure RVs cost = 2,300 + 0.28m	*Roadmaster RVs* cost = 1,900 + 0.36m
= 2,300 + 0.28(**5,010**)	= 1,900 + 0.36(**5,010**)
= 3,702.80	= 3,703.60

Since *Adventure RVs* rental cost of $3,702.80 is less than *Roadmaster RVs* rental cost of $3,703.60, the result seems reasonable.

ANSWERS TO SELF CHECKS

1. Yes **2.** $[0, \infty)$ **3.** $(-\infty, 1)$

4. a. $[-200, \infty)$ **b.** $(-\infty, 12)$

5. $(-3, \infty)$ **6.** $(-\infty, 2.1)$

7. $\left[\frac{13}{4}, \infty\right)$ **8.** $[-2, 1)$

9. $[-4, 0]$ **10.** 4,600 rpm or less   **11.** 84%

12. *Be Thrifty's* plan is better if the car is going to be driven more than 100 miles that day.

SECTION **4.8**   STUDY SET

VOCABULARY

Fill in the blanks.

1. An _____ is a statement that contains one of the symbols: $>$, $\geq$, $<$, or $\leq$.

2. To _____ an inequality means to find all the values of the variable that make the inequality true.

3. The solution set of $x > 2$ can be expressed in _____ notation as $(2, \infty)$.

4. The inequality $-4 < x \leq 10$ is an example of a _____ inequality.

CONCEPTS

Fill in the blanks.

5. a. Adding the _____ number to both sides of an inequality does not change the solutions.

   b. Multiplying or dividing both sides of an inequality by the same _____ number does not change the solutions.

   c. If we multiply or divide both sides of an inequality by a _____ number, the direction of the inequality symbol must be reversed for the inequalities to have the same solutions.

   d. To solve $-4 \leq 2x + 1 < 3$, properties of inequality are applied to all _____ parts of the inequality.

6. Rewrite the inequality $32 < x$ in an equivalent form with the variable on the left side.

7. The solution set of an inequality is graphed below. Which of the four numbers, 3, -3, 2, and 4.5, when substituted for the variable in that inequality, would make it true?

8. Insert the correct symbol, $<$, $\leq$, $>$, or $\geq$, in each blank.

   a. As many as 16 people were seriously injured: The number of people seriously injured ▢ 16.

   b. There were no fewer than 8 references to taxes in the speech: The number of tax references ▢ 8.

   c. The weight w of the roast is at most 8 pounds: w ▢ 8.

   d. The temperature t exceeded 100°: t ▢ 100.

NOTATION

9. Write each symbol.

   a. is less than or equal to

   b. infinity

   c. bracket

   d. is greater than

10. Consider the graph of the interval $[4, 8)$.

   a. Is the endpoint 4 included or not included in the graph?

   b. Is the endpoint 8 included or not included in the graph?

Complete the steps to solve each inequality.

11. $4x - 5 \geq 7$

   $4x - 5 + \boxed{} \geq 7 + \boxed{}$

   $4x \geq \boxed{}$

   $\dfrac{4x}{\boxed{}} \geq \dfrac{12}{\boxed{}}$

   $x \geq 3$ Solution set: $\left[\boxed{}, \infty \right)$

12. $-6x > 12$

   $\dfrac{-6x}{\boxed{}} \boxed{} \dfrac{12}{-6}$

   $x < \boxed{}$ Solution set: $\left(\boxed{}, -2 \right)$

GUIDED PRACTICE

See Example 1.

13. Determine whether each number is a solution of $3x - 2 > 5$.

   a. 5   **b.** -4

14. Determine whether each number is a solution of $3x + 7 < 4x - 2$.

   a. 12   **b.** 9

15. Determine whether each number is a solution of $-5(x - 1) \geq 2x + 12$.

   a. 1   **b.** -1

16. Determine whether each number is a solution of $\frac{4}{5}a \geq -2$.

   a. $-\dfrac{5}{4}$ **b.** -15

Graph each inequality and describe the graph using interval notation. See Example 2.

17. $x < 5$ **18.** $x \geq -2$

19. $-3 < x \leq 1$ **20.** $-4 \leq x \leq 2$

Write the inequality that is represented by each graph. Then describe the graph using interval notation.

21.
-1

22.
2

23.
-7 2

24.
4 6

Solve each inequality. Write the solution set in interval notation and graph it. See Examples 3–4.

25. $x + 2 > 5$

26. $x + 5 \geq 2$

27. $g - 30 \geq -20$

28. $h - 18 \leq -3$

29. $8h < 48$

30. $2t > 22$

31. $-\dfrac{3}{16}x \geq -9$

32. $-\dfrac{7}{8}x \leq 21$

33. $-3y \leq -6$

34. $-6y \geq -6$

35. $\dfrac{2}{3}x \geq 2$

36. $\dfrac{3}{4}x < 3$

Solve each inequality. Write the solution set in interval notation and graph it. See Examples 5–6.

37. $9x + 1 > 64$

38. $4x + 8 < 32$

39. $0.5 \geq 2x - 0.3$

40. $0.8 > 7x - 0.04$

41. $\dfrac{x}{8} - (-9) \geq 11$

42. $\dfrac{x}{6} - (-12) > 14$

43. $\dfrac{m}{-42} - 1 > -1$

44. $\dfrac{a}{-25} + 3 < 3$

45. $-x - 3 \leq 7$

46. $-x - 9 > 3$

47. $-3x - 7 > -1$

48. $-5x + 7 \leq 12$

Solve each inequality. Write the solution set in interval notation and graph it. See Example 7.

49. $9a + 4 > 5a - 16$

50. $8t + 1 < 4t - 19$

51. $0.4x \leq 0.1x + 0.45$

52. $0.9s \leq 0.3s + 0.54$

53. $8(5 - x) \leq 10(8 - x)$

54. $17(3 - x) \geq 3 - 13x$

55. $8x + 4 > -(3x - 4)$

56. $7x + 6 \geq -(x - 6)$

57. $\dfrac{1}{2} + \dfrac{n}{5} > \dfrac{3}{4}$

58. $\dfrac{1}{3} + \dfrac{c}{5} > -\dfrac{3}{2}$

59. $\dfrac{6x + 1}{4} \leq x + 1$

60. $\dfrac{3x - 10}{5} \leq x + 4$

Solve each compound inequality. Write the solution set in interval notation and graph it. See Examples 8–9.

61. $2 < x - 5 < 5$

62. $-8 < t - 8 < 8$

63. $0 \leq x + 10 \leq 10$

64. $-9 \leq x + 8 < 1$

65. $-3 \le \dfrac{c}{2} \le 5$ **66.** $-12 < \dfrac{b}{3} < 0$

87. $7 < \dfrac{5}{3}a + (-3)$ **88.** $5 < \dfrac{7}{2}a + (-9)$

67. $3 \le 2x - 1 < 5$ **68.** $4 < 3x - 5 \le 7$

89. $-8 \le \dfrac{y}{8} - 4 \le 2$ **90.** $6 < \dfrac{m}{16} + 7 < 8$

69. $-9 < 6x + 9 \le 45$ **70.** $-30 \le 10d + 20 < 90$

91. $-2(2x - 3) > 17$ **92.** $-3(x + 0.2) < 0.3$

71. $6 < -2(x - 1) < 12$ **72.** $4 \le -4(x - 2) < 20$

93. $\dfrac{5}{3}(x + 1) \ge -x + \dfrac{2}{3}$ **94.** $\dfrac{5}{2}(7x - 15) \ge \dfrac{11}{2}x - \dfrac{3}{2}$

TRY IT YOURSELF

Solve each inequality or compound inequality. Write the solution set in interval notation and graph it.

95. $2x + 9 \le x + 8$ **96.** $3x + 7 \le 4x - 2$

73. $6 - x \le 3(x - 1)$ **74.** $3(3 - x) \ge 6 + x$

97. $-7x + 1 < -5$ **98.** $-3x - 10 \ge -5$

75. $\dfrac{y}{4} + 1 \le -9$ **76.** $\dfrac{r}{8} - 7 \ge -8$

LOOK ALIKES . . .

solve each equation and inequality. Write the solution set of each inequality in interval notation and graph it.

77. $0 < 5(x + 2) \le 15$ **78.** $-18 \le 9(x - 5) < 27$

99. **a.** $\dfrac{3}{8} + \dfrac{b}{3} > \dfrac{5}{12}$ **b.** $\dfrac{3}{8} + \dfrac{b}{3} = \dfrac{5}{12}$

100. **a.** $7(a - 3) < 2(5a - 8)$ **b.** $7(a - 3) = 2(5a - 8)$

79. $-1 \le -\dfrac{1}{2}n$ **80.** $-3 \ge -\dfrac{1}{3}t$

101. **a.** $4 \le 2x - 6$ **b.** $4 \le 2x - 6 < 18$

81. $-m - 12 > 15$ **82.** $-t + 5 < 10$

102. **a.** $-16 < 4(x + 8) \le 8$ **b.** $-16 = 4(x + 8) + 8$

CONCEPT EXTENSIONS

Solve the inequality in part a. Graph the solution set and write it in interval notation. Then use your answer to part a to determine the solution set for the inequality in part b. (No new work is necessary!) Graph the solution set and write it in interval notation.

83. $-\dfrac{2}{3} \ge \dfrac{2y}{3} - \dfrac{3}{4}$ **84.** $-\dfrac{2}{9} \ge \dfrac{5x}{6} - \dfrac{1}{3}$

103. **a.** $12x - 33.16 \le 5.84$ **b.** $12x - 33.16 > 5.84$

85. $9x + 13 \ge 2x + 6x$ **86.** $7x - 16 < 2x + 4x$

104. **a.** $-\dfrac{3}{4}x > -\dfrac{21}{32}$ **b.** $-\dfrac{3}{4}x \le -\dfrac{21}{32}$

105. a. $3(2x + 2) > 5(x - 1) + 3x$

　　b. $3(2x + 2) < 5(x - 1) + 3x$

106. a. $\dfrac{x - 3}{2} \leq \dfrac{1}{2} - \dfrac{x - 5}{4}$　　**b.** $\dfrac{x - 3}{2} > \dfrac{1}{2} - \dfrac{x - 5}{4}$

APPLICATIONS

107.

Heating, Ventilation, and Air Conditioning

The percent of the air-borne particles in a room that a Climatec® furnace filter can remove is approximated by the formula $p = \frac{6}{5}m$, where m is the time in minutes that the furnace has been operating. Use an inequality to determine the time after which at least 60% of the air-borne particles in the room will have been removed. (Source: climatec.com)

108. WIKIPEDIA The number of articles a in millions in the English-language edition of Wikipedia can be approximated by the formula $a = 0.54t + 0.5$, where t is the number of years since 2005. Use an inequality to determine those years for which the number of articles surpassed 2.5 million. (Source: Wikipedia article: *Size of Wikipedia*)

The Wikipedia logo and trademark are used by permission from the Wikipedia Foundation.

109. NATIONAL PARKS The number of visitors v to U.S. national parks can be approximated by the formula $v = -100{,}000t + 3{,}600{,}000$, where t is the number of years after 1990. Use an inequality to determine those years for which the number of visitors fell below 2,400,000. (Source: National Park Service Stats)

110. MEDICARE The number of workers w for each Medicare beneficiary (each person receiving Medicare benefits) is approximated by the formula $w = -0.05t + 4$, where t is the number of years after 2000. Use an inequality to determine those years for which there will be less than 2 workers for each Medicare beneficiary. (Source: Kaiser Family Foundation)

111. GRADES A student has test scores of 68%, 75%, and 79% in a government class. What must she score on the last exam to earn a B (80% or better) in the course?

112. OCCUPATIONAL TESTING An employment agency requires applicants average at least 70% on a battery of four job skills tests. If an applicant scored 70%, 74%, and 84% on the first three exams, what must he score on the fourth test to maintain a 70% or better average?

113. GAS MILEAGE A car manufacturer produces three models in equal quantities. One model has an economy rating of 17 miles per gallon, and the second model is rated for 19 mpg. If government regulations require the manufacturer to have a fleet average that exceeds 21 mpg, what economy rating is required for the third model?

114. SERVICE CHARGES When the average daily balance of a customer's checking account falls below $500 in any week, the bank assesses a $5 service charge. The table shows the daily balances of one customer. What must Friday's balance be to avoid the service charge?

Day	Balance
Monday	$540.00
Tuesday	$435.50
Wednesday	$345.30
Thursday	$310.00

115. GEOMETRY The perimeter of an equilateral triangle is at most 57 feet. What could the length of a side be? (*Hint:* All three sides of an equilateral triangle are equal.)

116. GEOMETRY The perimeter of a square is no less than 68 centimeters. How long can a side be?

117. COUNTER SPACE A rectangular counter is being built for the customer service department of a store. Designers have determined that the outside perimeter of the counter (shown in red) needs to exceed 30 feet. Determine the acceptable values for x.

x ft

$(x + 5)$ ft

Customer Service

Customer Service

118. NUMBER PUZZLES What numbers satisfy the condition: Four more than three times the number is at most 10?

119. GRADUATIONS It costs a student $18 to rent a cap and gown and 80 cents for each graduation announcement that she orders. If she doesn't want her spending on these graduation costs to exceed $50, how many announcements can she order?

120. VIDEO GAME SYSTEMS A student who can afford to spend up to $1,000 sees the ad shown in the illustration and decides to buy the video game system. Use an inequality to find the greatest number of video games that she can also purchase. (Disregard sales tax.)

121. WINDOWS An architect needs to design a triangular-shaped bathroom window that has an area no greater than 100 in.². If the base of the window must be 16 inches long, what window heights will meet this condition?

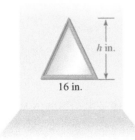

122. ROOM TEMPERATURES To hold the temperature of a room between 19° and 22° Celsius, what Fahrenheit temperatures must be maintained? $\left(\text{Hint: Use the formula } C = \frac{5}{9}(F - 32).\right)$

123. MOVING DAY *Valley Truck Rentals* charges $25.50 per day and $0.75 per mile to rent a 14-foot truck. *Nationwide Truck Rentals'* daily charge for the same vehicle is $36.75 and $0.60 per mile. If the truck is rented for one day, for what range of miles driven is *Nationwide's* plan better?

124. TELEPHONE SERVICE A telephone company offers two long-distance calling plans.

- Plan 1: $17 per month and 2¢ per minute
- Plan 2: $8 per month and 8¢ per minute

For how many minutes of long distance calls would Plan 2 save the caller money?

125. BUSINESS LOSSES It costs a company $1,400 to set up the necessary machinery and then $5 each to manufacture bath towels. They sell the towels for $8.50 each. Up to this point, the company has lost money on the towels. What is the greatest number of towels they could have sold for this to happen?

126. JOB OFFERS A company has offered a newly hired salesperson her choice of compensation packages:

- Package 1: $2,500 salary per month and a 5% sales commission
- Package 2: $3,500 salary per month and a 3% sales commission

What amount of sales per month would the salesperson have to make so that Package 1 is more profitable for her?

127. EXERCISE The graph in the next column shows the target heart beat range for different ages and exercise intensity levels. If we let b represent the number of beats per minute, then the compound inequality that estimates the heart beat rate range for a 30-year-old involved in a high-intensity workout is about $168 \leq b \leq 198$. Use a compound inequality to estimate the heart beat rate range for the following ages and zones.

a. 45-year-old, fat-burning zone

b. 70-year-old, high-intensity zone

c. 25-year-old, intermediate zone

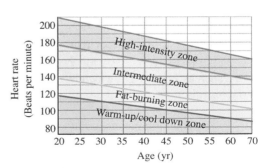

Source: elitefitness.co.nz

128. NUMBER PUZZLES What *whole* numbers satisfy the condition: Twice the number decreased by 1 is between 50 and 60?

WRITING

129. Explain why multiplying both sides of an inequality by a negative number reverses the direction of the inequality.

130. Explain the use of parentheses and brackets for graphing intervals.

131. How are the methods for solving linear equations and linear inequalities similar? How are they different?

132. Explain how the symbol ∞ is used in this section. Is ∞ a real number?

133. Explain what is wrong with the following statement:

When solving inequalities involving negative numbers, the direction of the inequality symbol must be reversed.

134. In each case, determine what is wrong with the interval notation.
    a. $(\infty, -3)$ **b.** $[-\infty, -3)$

MODULE 4 TEST

1. Fill in the blanks.
   a. _____ are letters (or symbols) that stand for numbers.
   b. A number, such as 8, is called a _____ because it does not change.
   c. Variables and/or numbers can be combined with the operations of arithmetic to create algebraic _____.
   d. A ____ is a product or quotient of numbers and/or variables. Examples are: $8x$, $\frac{t}{2}$, and $-cd^3$.
   e. Addition symbols separate algebraic expressions into parts called _____.
   f. A term, such as 27, that consists of a single number is called a _____ term.
   g. The _____ of the term $10x$ is 10.
   h. To _____ $4x - 3$ for $x = 5$, we substitute 5 for x and perform the necessary calculations.
   i. An _____ is a mathematical sentence that contains an = symbol. An algebraic _____ does not.
   j. To perform the multiplication $3(x + 4)$, we use the _____ property.
   k. Terms such as $7x^2$ and $5x^2$, which have the same variables raised to exactly the same power, are called ____ terms.
   l. To _____ an equation means to find all values of the variable that make the equation true.
   m. When we write $4x + x$ as $5x$, we say we have _____ like terms.
   n. To _____ the solution of an equation, we substitute the value for the variable in the original equation and determine whether the result is a true statement.

   o. The _____ property of _____ says that multiplying both sides of an equation by the same nonzero number does not change its solution.
   p. A _____ is an equation that states a mathematical relationship between two or more variables.
   q. The formula $a = P - b - c$ is _____ for a because a is isolated on one side of the equation and the other side does not contain a.
   r. An _____ is a statement that contains one of the symbols $>$, $\geq$, $<$, or $\leq$.

2. Consider the expression $3x^3 + 11x^2 - x + 9$.
   a. How many terms does the expression have?
   b. What is the coefficient of each term?

3. Complete the following table.

Term	$6m$	$-75t$	w	$\frac{1}{2}bh$	$\frac{x}{5}$	t
Coefficient						

4. Determine whether the variable c is used as a factor or as a term.
   a. $c + 32$ **b.** $-24c + 6$
   c. $5c$ **d.** $a + b + c$

5 a. The illustration below shows the distances from two towns to an airport. Which town is closer to the airport? How much closer is it?

$(x - 250)$ mi x mi

Brandon   Airport   Mill City

b. See the illustration below. Let *h* represent the height of the ladder, and write an algebraic expression for the height of the ceiling in feet.

6. Translate each of the following phrases to an algebraic expression.
  a. Five less than *n*
  b. The product of 7 and *x*
  c. The quotient of six and *p*
  d. The sum of *s* and −15
  e. Twice the length *l*
  f. *D* reduced by 100
  g. Two more than *r*
  h. 45 divided by *x*
  i. 100 reduced by twice the cutoff score *s*
  j. The absolute value of the difference of 2 and the square of *a*
  k. The product of *d* and 4, decreased by 15

7. Translate each algebraic expression into an English phrase. (Answers may vary.)
  a. $\dfrac{3}{4}r$
  b. $\dfrac{2}{3}d$
  c. $t - 50$
  d. $c + 19$

8. HARDWARE Refer to the illustration below.
  a. Let *n* represent the length of the nail (in inches). Write an algebraic expression that represents the length of the bolt (in inches).
  b. Let *b* represent the length of the bolt (in inches). Write an algebraic expression that represents the length of the nail (in inches).

4 in.

9. RETAINING WALLS The illustration in the next column shows the design for a retaining wall. The relationships between the lengths of its important parts are given in words.
  a. Choose a variable to represent one unknown dimension of the wall. Then write algebraic expressions to represent the lengths of the other two parts.

b. Suppose engineers determine that a 10-foot-high wall is needed. Find the lengths of the upper and lower bases.

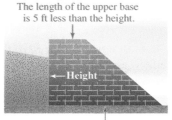

The length of the upper base is 5 ft less than the height.

←Height

The length of the lower base is 3 ft less than twice the height

10. Translate each of the following to an expression, an equation, or an inequality. Answers may vary depending upon the variable chosen.
  a. The weight of a truck exceeds 12,000 pounds.
  b. Three times a number is fifty-seven.
  c. Four times a number, subtracted from 6, is less than twice the number.
  d. Let *x* = Jane's age. Her sister, Julie, is 6 years older. Represent Julie's age.

11. CHILD CARE A child care center has six rooms, and the same number of children are in each room. If *c* children attend the center, write an algebraic expression that represents the number of children in each room.

12. CAR SALES A used car, originally advertised for $1,000, did not sell. The owner decided to drop the price $*x*. Write an algebraic expression that represents the new price of the car (in dollars).

13. CLOTHES DESIGNERS The legs on a pair of pants are *x* inches long. The designer then lets the hem down 1 inch. Write an algebraic expression that represents the new length (in inches) of the pants legs.

14. BUTCHERS A roast weighs *p* pounds. A butcher trimmed the roast into 8 equal-sized servings. Write an algebraic expression that represents the weight (in pounds) of one serving.

15. ROAD TRIPS On a cross-country vacation, a husband drove for twice as many hours as his wife. Choose a variable to represent the hours driven by one of them. Then write an algebraic expression to represent the hours driven by the other.

16. GEOMETRY The length of a rectangle is 3 units more than its width. Choose a variable to represent one of the dimensions. Then write an algebraic expression that represents the other dimension.

17. SPORTS EQUIPMENT An NBA basketball weighs 2 ounces more than twice the weight of a volleyball. Let a variable represent the weight of one of the sports balls. Then write an algebraic expression that represents the weight of the other ball.

18. BEST-SELLING BOOKS *The Lord of the Rings* was first published 6 years before *To Kill a Mockingbird*. *The Godfather* was first published 9 years after *To Kill a Mockingbird*. Write algebraic expressions to represent the ages of each of those books.

19. SALARIES A wife's monthly salary is $1,000 less than twice her husband's monthly salary.

   a. If her husband's monthly salary is h dollars, write an algebraic expression that represents the wife's monthly salary (in dollars).

   b. Suppose the husband's monthly salary is $2,350. Find the wife's monthly salary.

20. Use a table to help answer the following problem.

   a. How many eggs are in x dozen?

   b. d days is how many weeks?

Evaluate each expression.

21. $x - 16$ for $x = 4$

22. $2t^2 - 3(t - s)$ for $t = -2$ and $s = 4$

23. $-a^2 + 10$ for $a = -3$

24. $\left| \dfrac{-10d + f^3}{-f} \right|$ for $d = -1$ and $f = -5$

25. Complete the table.

x	$2x - \dfrac{30}{x}$
5	
10	
−30	

26. Complete the table.

Type of coin	Number	Value (¢)	Total value (¢)
Nickel	6		
Dime	d		

27. Find the volume, to the nearest tenth of a cubic inch, of the ice cream waffle cone shown in the next column by evaluating the algebraic expression

$$\dfrac{\pi r^2 h}{3}$$

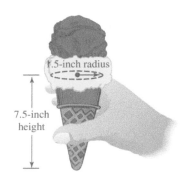

1.5-inch radius

7.5-inch height

28. Explain the difference between an expression and an equation. Give an example of each.

29. Use the given property to complete each statement.

   a. $(-12 + 97) + 3 = $ _____ Associative property of addition

   b. $2(x + 7) = $ _____ Distributive property

   c. $-2(m)5 = $ _____ Commutative property of multiplication

30. ROBOTS Find an algebraic expression that represents the total length (in feet) of the robotic arm shown below.

$(x + 4)$ ft

$(x - 1)$ ft

x ft

Simplify each expression.

31. $5(-4x)$

32. $-8(-7t)(4)$

33. $\dfrac{4}{5}(15a + 5) - 16a$

34. $-1.1d^2 - 3.8d^2 - d^2$

35. $9x^2 + 2(7x - 3) - 9(x^2 - 1)$

36. $n + n + n + n$

37. $5(p - 2) - 2(3p + 4)$

38. $8a^3 + 4a^3 + 2a - 4a^3 - 2a - 1$

39. $\dfrac{3}{5}w - \left(-\dfrac{2}{5}w\right)$

40. Write an expression that represents the perimeter of the rectangle.

$5x$ feet

$(4x + 3)$ feet

41. Is 3 a solution of $5y + 2 = 127$

42. Draw a series of scales to illustrate how to solve $3x + 2 = x + 6$.

Solve each equation.

43. $3h + 2 = 8$

44. $\dfrac{4}{5}t = -4$

45. $-22 = -x$

46. $\dfrac{11b - 11}{5} = 3b - 2$

47. $0.8(x - 1,000) + 1.3 = 2.9 + 0.2x$

48. $2(y - 7) - 3y = -(y - 3) - 17$

49. $\dfrac{m}{2} - \dfrac{1}{3} = \dfrac{1}{4} + \dfrac{m}{6}$

50. $9 - 5(2x + 10) = -1$

51. $24t = -6(8 - 4t)$

52. $6a + (-7) = 3a - 7 + 2a$

53. Solve the following equations and describe the solution of each using full sentences. Use the words conditional, identity, and contradiction in your answers.
  a. $4(x + 5) - 8 = 4x + 12$

  b. $4(x + 5) - 8 = 4x - 11$

  c. $4(x + 5) - 8 = 5x - 12$

54. RESTAURANTS One month, a restaurant had sales of $13,500 and made a profit of $1,700. Find the expenses for the month.

55. SNAILS A typical garden snail travels at an average rate of 2.5 feet per minute. How long would it take a snail to cross a 20-feet long flower bed?

56. CERTIFICATES OF DEPOSIT A $26,000 investment in a CD earned $1,170 in interest the first year. What was the annual interest rate?

57. JEWELRY Gold melts at about 1,065°C. Change this to degrees Fahrenheit.

58. CAMPING
  a. Find the perimeter of the air mattress shown below
  b. Find the amount of sleeping area on the top surface of the air mattress.
  c. Find the approximate volume of the air mattress if it is 3 inches thick.

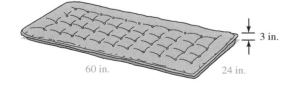

60 in.   24 in.   3 in.

59. Find the area of a triangle with a base 17 meters long and a height of 9 meters.

60. a. Find the circumference of a circle with a radius of 8 centimeters. Round to the nearest hundredth of one centimeter.
  b. Find the area of the circle. Round to the nearest square centimeter.

Solve for the specified variable.

61. $V = \pi r^2 h$ for h

62. $A = P + Prt$ for r

63. $A = \dfrac{a + b + c + d}{4}$ for c

64. $2x - 3y = 9$ for y

65. RENEWABLE ENERGY Apple's data center in Maiden, North Carolina, will use about 20 megawatts of power at full capacity. Some of that power will be purchased directly from renewable energy sources in the region. Most of the power will be produced onsite from renewable sources such as solar arrays and fuel cells. The amount of energy made onsite will be 4 megawatts less than twice the amount purchased from regional sources. How many megawatts of power will come from regional sources and how many will be produced onsite? (Source: apple.com)

66. HOME SALES A condominium owner cleared $114,600 on the sale of his condo, after paying a 4.5% real estate commission. What was the selling price?

67. COLORADO The state of Colorado is approximately rectangular-shaped with a perimeter of 1,320 miles. Find the length (east to west) and width (north to south), if the length is 100 miles longer than the width.

68. TEA How many pounds of green tea, worth $40 a pound, should be mixed with herbal tea, worth $50 a pound, to produce 20 pounds of a blend worth $42 a pound?

69. READING A bookmark is inserted between two page numbers whose sum is 825. What are the page numbers?

70. SIGNING PETITIONS A professional signature collector is paid $50 a day plus $2.25 for each verified signature he gets from a registered voter. How many signatures are needed to earn $500 a day?

71. TRAVEL TIMES A car leaves Rockford, Illinois, at the rate of 65 mph, bound for Madison, Wisconsin. At the same time, a truck leaves Madison at the rate of 55 mph, bound for Rockford. If the cities are 72 miles apart, how long will it take for the car and the truck to meet?

72. PICKLES To make pickles, fresh cucumbers are soaked in a salt water solution called *brine*. How many liters of a 2% brine solution must be added to 30 liters of a 10% brine solution to dilute it to an 8% solution?

73. GEOMETRY If the vertex angle of an isosceles triangle is 44°, find the measure of each base angle.

74. INVESTMENTS Part of $13,750 is invested at 9% annual interest, and the rest is invested at 8%. After one year, the accounts paid $1,185 in interest. How much was invested at the lower rate?

75. AIRPLANES How long will it take a jet plane, flying at 450 mph, to overtake a propeller plane, flying at 180 mph, if the propeller plane had a $2\frac{1}{2}$-hour head start?

76. AUTOGRAPHS Kesha collected the autographs of 8 more television celebrities than she has of movie stars. Each TV celebrity autograph is worth $75 and each movie star autograph is worth $250. If her collection is valued at $1,900, how many of each type of autograph does she have?

Solve each inequality. Write the solution set in interval notation and graph it.

77. $-8x - 20 \le 4$

78. $-8.1 > \frac{1}{2}x + (-11.3)$

79. $-12 \le 2(x + 1) < 10$

80. $\frac{x}{4} - \frac{1}{3} > \frac{5}{6} + \frac{x}{3}$

81. AWARDS A city honors its citizen of the year with a framed certificate. An artist charges $15 for the frame and 75 cents per word for writing out the proclamation. If a city regulation does not allow gifts in excess of $150, what is the maximum number of words that can be written on the certificate?

82. ICE SKATING For the free-skating portion of a competition, an ice skater received scores of 5.3, 4.8, 4.7, 4.9, and 5.1 from the first five judges. What score must she receive from the sixth and final judge to average better than 5.0 for her performance?

83. INSURANCE COVERAGE A fire damage restoration crew charges $175 for the first hour of cleanup and $80 for each additional hour or part there of. For how long can the crew work at a home with smoke and water damage if the homeowner's insurance policy will only cover up to $1,000 of the cleanup cost?

84. MEDICAL SCHOOLS The number of women graduating annually from U.S. medical schools w can be approximated by the formula $w = 150t + 5,200$, where t is the number of years after 1990. Use an inequality to determine those years for which the number of women graduating from medical school was at most 6,550. (Source: Wikipedia article: AAMC)

85. JOB OFFERS A recent graduate of a culinary school has job offers from two local bakeries.
- Corner Bakery: $15.50 an hour but employee must purchase $135 worth of uniforms to start
- Main Street Bakery: $12.80 an hour, uniforms are provided by employer

How many hours must be worked at the Corner Bakery for it to be at least as profitable as working at Main Street Bakery?

86. VACATION RENTALS Janice has $2,040 in a savings account at the beginning of the summer. She wants to have at least $500 in the account by the end of the summer to pay her part of a beach house rental. She withdraws $140 each week for food, clothes, entertainment, and other expenses. How many weeks can Janice withdraw from her savings account and have at least $500 left?

87. FUNDRAISERS The revenue received for selling x tubs of cookie dough for a school fundraiser is given by the formula $R = 12x$. The cost C to the school for x tubs of cookie dough is $C = 5.75x + 1,500$. Write and solve an inequality to find the number of tubs that need to be sold so that the school makes a profit.

88. SPORTS EQUIPMENT The acceptable weight w of Ping-Pong balls used in competition can range from 2.40 to 2.53 grams. Express this range using a compound inequality.

Module 4 Answers

Are You Ready? Section 4.1 (Page 4)

1. $9x$ **2.** m **3.** $-t$ **4.** $\frac{7}{8}y$ **5.** Quotient
6. Difference **7.** Product **8.** Sum

Study Set Section 4.1 (Page 13)

1. evaluate **3.** expression, equation **5.** $6 + 20x$, $\frac{6-x}{20}$
(answers may vary) **7.** We would obtain $34 - 6$; it looks
like 34, not 3(4) **9. a.** $2x - 500$ **b.** 3,500 lb **11.** 5, 30,
10, 10d, 50, 50$(x + 5)$ **13.** 5, 5, 25, 45 **15.** 4, -5, 7
17. 9, -4 **19.** term **21.** factor **23.** $l + 15$ **25.** $50x$
27. $\frac{w}{l}$ **29.** $P + p$ **31.** $k^2 - 2{,}005$ **33.** $J - 500$ **35.** $\frac{1{,}000}{n}$
37. $p + 90$ **39.** $(x + 2)$ in. **41.** $x + 150$ **43.** $\frac{c}{6}$
45. $\frac{x}{2}$ **47.** $5b$ **49.** $2w$ **51.** x ft, $(12 - x)$ ft **53.** $2x + 25$
55. a. x = age of Apple, $x + 80$ = age of IBM, $x - 9$ = age
of Dell **b.** IBM:112 years, Dell:23 years **57.** Illinois: x,
Florida: $x + 27$, California: $x + 32$ **59. a.** 300 **b.** $60h$
61. a. $3y$ **b.** $\frac{f}{3}$ **63.** -12 **65.** 20 **67.** 156 **69.** -5
71. $-\frac{1}{5}$ **73.** -2 **75.** 17 **77.** 230 **79.** $-1, -2, -28$
81. 41, 11, 2 **83.** 150, -450 **85.** 0, 0, 5 **87.** $35 + h + 300$
89. $p - 680$ **91.** $4d - 15$ **93.** $2(200 + t)$ **95.** $|a - 2|$
97. $2x + 4$ **99. a.** $x + 7^2$ **b.** $(x + 7)^2$ **101. a.** $4(x + 2)$
b. $4x + 2$ **103.** $-2, 2$ **105.** $2a$ **107.** 0, 48, 64, 48, 0
109. $-37°C, -64°C$ **111.** $1\frac{23}{64}$ in.^{2} **113.** 235 ft^2

Applications Introduction : Properties of Real Numbers Section 4.2 (Page 19)

1. a. commutative property of addition **b.** associative
property of addition **c.** associative property of addition
d. commutative property of addition **2. a.** associative
property of multiplication **b.** commutative property of
multiplication **c.** associative property of multiplication
d. commutative property of multiplication **3. a.** $111,
$25, $16 $100, $300 **b.** commutative and associative
properties of addition **4. a.** 20 meters, $(x + 6)$ meters,
$20 (x + 6)$ square meters **b.** 20 meters, x meters,
$20x$ square meters **c.** 20 meters, 6 meters, 120 square meters
d. $20 (x + 6)$, $20 x$, 120 **5. a.** 5 6, 6, 2, 3

Are You Ready? Section 4.2 (Page 21)

1. The terms are in a different order **2.** The position of
the parentheses is different **3.** 30, 30; same result
4. Different variable factors (x and y); the same
coefficient (4)

Study Set Section 4.2 (Page 29)

1. simplify **3.** distributive **5. a.** 4, 9, 36
b. Associative property of multiplication **7.** distributive
property **9.** $ab + ac + ad$ **11. a.** $-$ **b.** $+$ **c.** $-$ **d.** $+$
13. 7, 7, 14 **15. a.** no **b.** yes **17. a.** $5x + 1$ **b.** $16t - 6$
19. $(8 + 7) + a$ **21.** $11y$ **23.** $8d(2 \cdot 6)$ **25.** $(t + 4)$
27. $63m$ **29.** $-35q$ **31.** $5x$ **33.** $20bp$ **35.** $40r^2$
37. $48q^2$ **39.** $5x + 15$ **41.** $-2b + 2$ **43.** $24t - 16$
45. $-15t - 12$ **47.** $-r + 10$ **49.** $-x + 7$ **51.** $-2w + 4$
53. $6x - 2y$ **55.** $34x - 17y + 34$ **57.** $1.4 - 0.3p + 0.1t$
59. $8p, -5p$ **61.** no like terms **63.** $20x$ **65.** $3x^2$
67. 0 **69.** 0 **71.** $1.1h - 2p$ **73.** $2a + b$ **75.** $x + 3y$
77. $-11x^2 - 3y^2$ **79.** $b + 2$ **81.** $-2x^2 + 3x$ **83.** $-3c - 1$
85. $2c + 9$ **87.** $0.4x - 1.6$ **89.** $7X - 2x$ **91.** $-3x$
93. t **95.** $\frac{4}{5}t$ **97.** $12y - 6$ **99.** $7y - 5$ **101.** $6y$
103. $0.4r$ **105.** $7z - 15$ **107.** $12c + 34$ **109.** $-96m$
111. 0 **113.** $8x{-}9$ **115.** Doesn't simplify **117.** $a^3 - 8$
119. a. $10x$ **b.** can't be simplified **121. a.** $18x$ **b.** $3x + 5$
123. a. $480n$ **b.** $96n + 60$ **125. a.** $18a$ **b.** Does not simplify
127. $11x$, 7 **129.** 378 **131.** $x + 20 - x = 20$, 20 ft
133. yes

Applications Introduction : Properties of Equality Section 4.3 (Page 33)

1. d. same **2. d.** same **3. d.** same **4. d.** same

Are You Ready? Section 4.3 (Page 35)

1. $-$ **2.** $+$ **3.** 7 **4.** $\cdot$ **5.** $\frac{2}{5}$ **6.** $-\frac{8}{9}$

Study Set Section 4.3 (Page 43)

1. equation **3.** solve **5.** equivalent **7. a.** $x + 6$
b. neither **c.** no **d.** yes **9.** c, c **b.** c, c **11. a.** x **b.** y
c. t **d.** h **13.** 5, 5, 50 50, $\underline{2}$, 45, 50 **15. a.** is possibly
equal to **b.** yes **17.** no **19.** no **21.** no **23.** no **25.** yes
27. no **29.** no **31.** yes **33.** yes **35.** yes **37.** 71
39. 18 **41.** -0.9 **43.** 3 **45.** $\frac{8}{9}$ **47.** 3 **49.** $-\frac{1}{25}$
51. -2.3 **53.** 45 **55.** 0 **57.** 21 **59.** -2.64 **61.** 20
63. 15 **65.** -6 **67.** 4 **69.** 4 **71.** 7 **73.** 1 **75.** -6
77. 20 **79.** 0.5 **81.** -18 **83.** $-\frac{4}{21}$ **85.** 13 **87.** 2.5
89. $-\frac{8}{3}$ **91.** $\frac{13}{40}$ **93.** 4 **95.** -5 **97.** -200 **99.** 95
101. 0 **103.** 0 **105.** 1 **107. a.** $\frac{13}{20}$ **b.** $\frac{17}{20}$ **c.** $\frac{15}{2}$
d. $\frac{3}{40}$ **109.** $x + 2 = 7; x = 5$ **113.** $65°$ **115.** $6,000,000

Are You Ready? Section 4.4 (Page 46)

1. -12 **2.** $2a$ **3.** $-7m + 18$ **4.** $3x$ **5.** $24n$ **6.** 8

Study Set Section 4.4 (Page 53)

1. equation **3.** conditional **5.** subtraction, multiplication **7. a.** $-2x - 8 = -24$ **b.** $-20 = 3x - 16$ **9. a.** $12x$ **b.** $2x$ **11.** 10 **13.** $+7, +7, 2, 2, 14, \underline{2}, 28, 21, 14$ **15.** 6 **17.** 5 **19.** -7 **21.** 18 **23.** 16 **25.** 12 **27.** $\frac{10}{3}$ **29.** $-\frac{5}{2}$ **31.** 5 **33.** -0.25 **35.** 2.9 **37.** -4 **39.** $\frac{11}{5}$ **41.** -1 **43.** -6 **45.** 0.04 **47.** -6 **49.** -11 **51.** 7 **53.** -11 **55.** 1 **57.** $\frac{9}{2}$ **59.** 3 **61.** -20 **63.** 6 **65.** $\frac{2}{15}$ **67.** $-\frac{12}{5}$ **69.** $\frac{27}{5}$ **71.** 5 **73.** 200 **75.** 1,000 **77.** 200 **79.** $\frac{5}{4}$ **81.** -1 **83.** 1 **85.** 80 **87.** all real numbers **89.** no solution **91.** no solution **93.** all real numbers **95.** $\frac{1}{4}$ **97.** 30 **99.** -11 **101.** no solution **103.** 1 **105.** $\frac{52}{9}$ **107.** -6 **109.** -5 **111.** 0 **113.** -0.5 **115. a.** $x - 20$ **b.** -5 **117. a.** $0.4 - 0.2x$ **b.** 0 **119. a.** $6x = 3x + 6$ **b.** $3x = 6, x = 2$ **121. a.** any real number greater than 4 **b.** any real number less than 4 **c.** 4

Are You Ready? Section 4.5 (Page 56)

1. a. one **b.** three **2.** d **3.** x **4.** $8c - cx$ **5.** Yes **6.** 1

Study Set Section 4.5 (Page 65)

1. formula **3.** volume **5. a.** $d = rt$ **b.** $r = c + m$ **c.** $p = r - c$ **d.** $I = Prt$ **7.** 11,176,920 mi, 65,280 ft **9.** Ax, Ax, B, B, B **11.** \$240 million **13.** \$931 **15.** 3.5% **17.** \$6,000 **19.** 2.5 mph **21.** 4.5 hours **23.** 185°C **25.** -454°F **27.** 20 in **29.** 1,885 mm^3 **31.** $c = r - m$ **33.** $b = P - a - c$ **35.** $R = \frac{E}{I}$ **37.** $l = \frac{V}{wh}$ **39.** $r = \frac{C}{2\pi}$ **41.** $h = \frac{3V}{B}$ **43.** $f = \frac{s}{w}$ **45.** $r = \frac{T - 2t}{2}$ **47.** $x = \frac{C - By}{A}$ **49.** $m = \frac{2K}{v^2}$ **51.** $c = 3A - a - b$ **53.** $t = T - 18E$ **55.** $r^2 = \frac{s}{4\pi}$ **57.** $v^2 = \frac{2Kg}{w}$ **59.** $r^3 = \frac{3V}{4\pi}$ **61.** $M = 4.2B + 19.8$ **63.** $h = \frac{S - 2\pi r^2}{2\pi r}$ **65.** $y = -3x + 9$ **67.** $y = \frac{1}{3}x + 3$ **69.** $y = -\frac{3}{4}x - 4$ **71.** $b = \frac{2A}{h} - d$ or $b = \frac{2A - hd}{h}$ **73.** $c = \frac{72 - 8w}{7}$ **75.** 87, 89, 91 **77.** 262.8, 247.1 **79.** 14 in. **81.** 50 in. **83.** Weight (lb) $= \dfrac{\text{BMI} \cdot \text{height}^2 (\text{in.}^2)}{703}$ **85.** Yes **87.** 113.4 cm^3, 7.1 in^3 **89.** 3,150 cm^2 **91.** 6 in

93. 8 ft **95.** $d = \frac{360A}{\pi(r_1^2 - r_2^2)}$, 140, 160

97. $n = \frac{C - 6.50}{0.07}$; 621, 1,000, about 1,692.9 kwh

99. $D = \dfrac{L - 3.25r - 3.25R}{2}$

Applications Introduction Let x = Section 4.6

2. How long did he wait three days ago?, Let $x =$ the number of minutes he waited three days ago **3.** Find the average lifespan of a Guinea pig, Let $x =$ the average life span of a Guinea pig (in years) **4.** what was her reading rate before taking the course?, Let $x =$ her reading rate before the course **5.** In how many years will she have 100 spoons in her collection?, Let $x =$ the number of years to have 100 spoons **6.** how many minutes of the program are shown in that one hour, Let $x =$ the number of minutes of the program shown in one hour **7.** How much of a 4% pesticide solution, Let $x =$ the amount of 4% pesticide needed (in gallons) **8.** Find the width (north to south), Let $x =$ the width (in miles) **9.** How many pounds of green tea, Let $x =$ the number of pounds of green tea needed **10.** how many payments will the amount she owes be reduced to \$420?, Let $x =$ the number of payments she must make to owe \$420

12. what is the measure of each base angle?,

13. What is the width of the court?

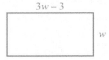

14. Find the measure of the angle at the stering column,

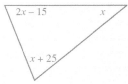

15. Find the length of the shorter piece,

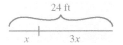

16. Find the length of the shortest section,

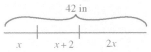

Are You Ready? Section 4.6 (Page 73)

1. $4x + 4$ **2.** 49 **3.** $39.15 **4.** $0.28x$ **5.** $P = 2l + 2w$
6. $180°$ **7.** $2x - 8$ **8.** 0.06

Study Set Section 4.6 (Page 79)

1. consecutive **3.** vertex, base **5.** 17, $x + 2$, $3x$
7. $0.03x **9.** $180°$ **11. a.** $x + 1$ **b.** $x + 2$ **13.** 4 ft, 8 ft
15. 276,000 acres **17.** 102 mi, 108 mi, 114 mi, 120 mi
19. 7.3 ft, 10.7 ft **21.** Guitar Hero: $2.99; Call of Duty:
World at War : Zombies II: $9.99; Tom Tom USA: $39.99
23. 250 calories in ice cream, 600 calories in pie **25.** 7
27. 580 **29.** 20 **31.** $50,000 **33.** $5,250 **35.** $240
37. Ronaldo: 15, Mueller: 14 **39.** *Friends: 236, Leave It
to Beaver: 234* **41.** July 22, 24, 26 **43.** width: 27 ft,
length: 78 ft **45.** 21 in. by 30.25 in. **47.** 7 ft, 7 ft, 11 ft
49. $20°$ **51.** $42.5°, 70°, 67.5°$ **53.** $22°, 68°$
55. Maximum stride angle: $106°$

Are You Ready? Section 4.7 (Page 83)

1. $400 **2.** 135 mi **3.** 3.6 gal of antifreeze **4.** $19.60
5. $14,000 **6.** $3x$

Study Set Section 4.7 (Page 91)

1. investment, motion **3.** $30,000 - x$ **5.** $r - 150$
7. $35t$, t, $45t$, 80, $35t + 45t = 80$ **9. a.** $0.50(6) + 0.25x = 0.30(6 + x)$, $0.50(6)$, $0.25x$, $6 + x$, $0.30(6 + x)$ **b.** $0.06x + 0.03(10 - x) = 0.05(10)$, $0.06x$, $10 - x$, $0.03(10 - x)$,
$0.05(10)$ **11.** 0.06, 0.152 **13.** 4 **15.** 6,000
17. $15,000 at 4%, $10,000 at 7% **19.** silver: $1,500,
gold: $2,000 **21.** $26,000 **23.** 822: $9,000, 721: $6,000
25. $4,900 **27.** $495, $495; $9,900 **29.** 2 hr
31. $\frac{1}{4}$ hr = 15 min **33.** 1 hr **35.** 4 hr **37.** 55 mph
39. 12 mi **41.** 50 gal **43.** 4%: 5 gal, 1%: 10 gal
45. 32 ounces of 8%, 32 ounces of 22% **47.** 6 gal
49. 28 lb **51.** 10 oz **53.** 50 lb **55.** 20 scoops **57.** 15
59. $4.25 **61.** 125 oz pure gold; 375 oz gold alloy
63. 17 **65.** 90 **67.** 40 pennies, 20 dimes,60 nickels
69. 2-pointers: 50, 3-pointers: 4 **71.** adult: 4 tickets,
seniors: 2 tickets, child: 1 ticket, military: 1 ticket

Applications Introduction : Inequalities Section 4.8 (Page 98)

1. a. 21 years old, 9 years old, 14 years old **b.** 35 years
old, 37 years old **c.** $<$ **2. a.** $ 3,151, $3,510, $5,031
b. $1,315, $3,150, $3,149 **c.** $>$ **3. a.** 56",54",61"
b. 53",47",50" **c.** $\geq$ **4. a.** 108 persons, 167 persons, 99
persons, 180 persons **b.** 190 persons, 181 persons **c.** $\leq$
6. Let p = the number of characters in the password; $p \geq 8$

7. Let w = the combined weight of the pet and carrier;
$w \leq 20$ **8.** Let n = the number of times the same extension
course is taken; $n > 2$ **9.** Let t = the time between
contractions; $t < 5$ **10.** Let h = the height of the tree
branch $h \leq 12$

Are You Ready? Section 4.8 (Page 100)

1. is, less, than **2.** True

3. **4.** $0 < 10$

Study Set Section 4.8 (Page 111)

1. inequality **3.** interval **5. a.** same **b.** positive
c. negative **d.** three **7.** 3,4,5 **9. a.** $\leq$ **b.** ∞ **c.** [or]
d. $>$ **11.** 5, 5, 12, 4, 4, 3 **13. a.** yes **b.** no **15. a.** no
b. yes **17.** $(-\infty, 5)$,

19. $(-3, 1]$

21. $x < -1$, $(-\infty, -1)$
23. $-7 < x \leq 2$, $(-7, 2]$
25. $(3, \infty)$,
27. $[10, \infty)$,
29. $(-\infty, 6)$,
31. $(-\infty, 48]$,
33. $[2, \infty)$,
35. $[3, \infty)$,
37. $(7, \infty)$,
39. $(-\infty, 0.4]$,
41. $[16, \infty)$,
43. $(-\infty, 0)$,
45. $[-10, \infty)$,
47. $(-\infty, -2)$,
49. $(-5, \infty)$,
51. $(-\infty, 1.5]$,
53. $(-\infty, 20]$,
55. $(0, \infty)$,

Answer Section 4

57. $\left(\frac{5}{4},\infty\right)$, — at 5/4

59. $\left(-\infty,\frac{3}{2}\right]$, — at 3/2

61. $(7, 10)$, — 7 to 10

63. $[-10, 0]$, — −10 to 0

65. $[-6, 10]$, — −6 to 10

67. $[2, 3)$, — 2 to 3

69. $(-3, 6]$, — −3 to 6

71. $(-5, -2)$, — −5 to −2

73. $\left[\frac{9}{4},\infty\right)$, — at 9/4

75. $(-\infty, -40]$, — at −40

77. $(-2, 1]$, — −2 to 1

79. $(-\infty, 2]$, — at 2

81. $(-\infty, -27)$, — at −27

83. $\left(-\infty,\frac{1}{8}\right]$, — at 1/8

85. $[-13,\infty)$, — at −13

87. $(6,\infty)$, — at 6

89. $[-32, 48]$, — −32 to 48

91. $\left(-\infty,-\frac{11}{4}\right)$, — at −11/4

93. $\left[-\frac{3}{8},\infty\right)$, — at −3/8

95. $(-\infty, -1]$, — at −1

97. $\left(\frac{6}{7},\infty\right)$, — at 6/7 **99. a.** $\left(\frac{1}{8},\infty\right)$ **b.** $\frac{1}{8}$

101. a. $[5,\infty)$ **b.** $[5, 12)$ **103. a.** $(-\infty, 3.25]$; **b.** $(3.25,\infty)$

105. a. $\left(-\infty,\frac{11}{2}\right)$; **b.** $\left(\frac{11}{2},\infty\right)$; **107.** 50 min or longer

109. Years after 2002 **111.** 98% or better **113.** more than 27 mpg **115.** 19 ft or less **117.** more than 5 ft **119.** 40 or less **121.** 12.5 in. or less **123.** More than 75 miles **125.** They could have sold as many as 399 towels **127.** (Answers may vary slightly.) **a.** $100 \le b \le 118$ **b.** $135 \le b \le 160$ **c.** $135 \le b \le 172$

Module 4 Test (Page 116)

1. a. Variables **b.** constant **c.** expressions **d.** term **e.** terms **f.** constant **g.** coefficient **h.** evaluate **i.** equation, expression **j.** distributive **k.** like **l.** solve **m.** combined **n.** check **o.** multiplication, equality **p.** formula **q.** solved **r.** inequality **2. a.** 4 **b.** 3, 11, − 1, 9 **3.** 6, − 75, 1, $\frac{1}{2}$, $\frac{1}{5}$, 1 **4. a.** Term **b.** Factor **c.** Factor **d.** Term

5. a. Brandon is closer by 250 mi,

$(x - 250)$ mi x mi

Brandon   Airport   Mill City **b.** $(h + 7)$ ft

6. a. $n - 5$, **b.** $7x$ **c.** $\frac{6}{p}$ **d.** $s + (-15)$ **e.** $2l$ **f.** $D - 100$ **g.** $r + 2$ **h.** $\frac{45}{x}$ **i.** $100 - 2s$ **j.** $|2 - a^2|$ **k.** $4d - 15$

7. a. Three-fourths of r **b.** Two-thirds of d **c.** 50 less than t **d.** 19 more than c **8. a.** $(n + 4)$ in **b.** $(b - 4)$ in **9. a.** h = the height of the wall, $h - 5$ the length of the upperbase, $2h - 3$ = the length of the lower base **b.** upper base:5 ft, lower base:17 ft **10. a.** $w > 12{,}000$ **b.** $3n = 57$ **c.** $6 - 4n < 2n$ **d.** $x + 6$ **11.** $\frac{c}{6}$ **12.** $\$(1{,}000 - x)$

13. $x + 1$ **14.** $\frac{p}{8}$ **15.** x = the number of hours driven by the wife, $2x$ = the number of hours driven by the husband **16.** w = the width, $w + 3$ = the length **17.** x = the weight of the volleyball (in ounces). $2x + 2$ = the weight of the NBA basketball (in ounces) **18.** x = *the age of To Kill a Mockingbird*, $x + 6$ the age of *The Lord of theRings*, $x - 9$ = the age of *The Godfather* **19. a.** $2h - 1{,}000$ **b.** $\$3{,}700$

20. a. $12x$ **b.** $\frac{d}{7}$ **21.** -12 **22.** 26 **23.** 1 **24.** 23 **25.** 4, 17, − 59 **26.** 5, 30, 10, $10d$ **27.** 17.7 in³ **28.** An equation is a mathematical sentence that contains an = sign. An expression does not contain an = sign. **29.** $-12 + (97 + 3)$ **b.** $2x + 14$ **c.** $-2(5)m$ **30.** $3x + 3$ **31.** $-20x$ **32.** $224t$ **33.** $-4a + 4$ **34.** $-5.9\,d^2$ **35.** $14x + 3$ **36.** $4n$ **37.** $-p - 18$ **38.** $8a^3 - 1$ **39.** w **40.** $(18x + 6)$ ft **41.** no **43.** 2 **44.** − 5 **45.** 22 **46.** $-\frac{1}{4}$ **47.** 1,336 **48.** all real numbers (an identity) **49.** $\frac{7}{4}$ **50.** − 4 **51.** no solution (a contradiction) **52.** 0 **53. a.** This equation is an identity. It is true for all real numbers. **b.** This equation is a contradiction. It is not true for any real number. **c.** This is a conditional equation. It is only true for $x = 24$ **54.** $\$11{,}800$ **55.** 8 min **56.** 4.5% **57.** 1,949°F **58. a.** 168 in **b.** 1,440 in² **c.** 4,320 in³ **59.** 76.5 m² **60. a.** 50.27 cm **b.** 201 cm² **61.** $h = \frac{V}{\pi r^2}$ **62.** $r = \frac{A-P}{Pt}$ **63.** $c = 4A - a - b - d$

64. $y = \frac{2}{3}x - 3$ **65.** regional sources:8 megawatts, on site: 12 megawatts   **66.** $120,000   **67.** 380 mi,280 mi   **68.** green: 16 lb, herbal: 4 lb   **69.** 412, 413   **70.** 200 signatures   **71.** $\frac{3}{5}$ hr or 36 min   **72.** 10 liters   **73.** 68°   **74.** $5,250   **75.** $1\frac{2}{3}$ hr, 1 hr 40 min   **76.** TV celebrities: 12 autographs; movie stars: 4 autographs

77. $[-3, \infty)$ **78.** $(-\infty, 6.4)$ **79.** $[-7, 4)$ **80.** $(-\infty, -14)$ **81.** 180 words   **82.** She needs to receive a score that is greater than 5.2   **83.** 11 hr   **84.** The years from 1990 through 1999   **85.** 50 hours or more   **86.** 11 weeks   **87.** $12x - (5.75x + 1,500) > 0$, A profit will be made if more than 240 tubs are sold   **88.** $2.40 \text{ g} \le w \le 2.53 \text{ g}$